PLANNING GUIDE

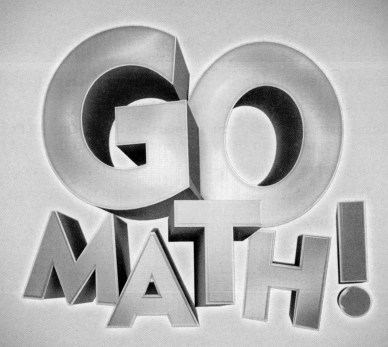

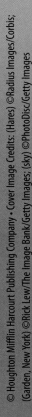
Copyright © 2015 by Houghton Mifflin Harcourt Publishing Company

ISBN 978-0-544-29330-4

8 9 10 11 12 13 14 0029 23 22 21 20 19 18 17 16
4500602313   CDEFG

Table of Contents

END-OF-YEAR RESOURCES

Review Projects

Getting Ready for Grade 1

These lessons review prerequisite skills and prepare for next year's content.

CORRELATIONS

It's Common Core Math

GO Math! for Kindergarten-Grade 6 combines powerful teaching strategies with never-before-seen components to offer everything needed to successfully teach and learn the Common Core State Standards.

that's perfect for 21st century students.

In the *GO Math!* classroom, teachers and students can choose a print-based approach, an online approach, or a blended learning approach. In each case, the focus is on the major work of the grade. The *GO Math!* team of authors carefully developed a coherent K–12 progression to help students connect concepts across and within grade levels. Whether you choose print or digital pathways, you'll find the rigor required for success with the Common Core.

Math on the Spot videos, available for every lesson in *GO Math!*, support teachers and students, within the classroom and at home.

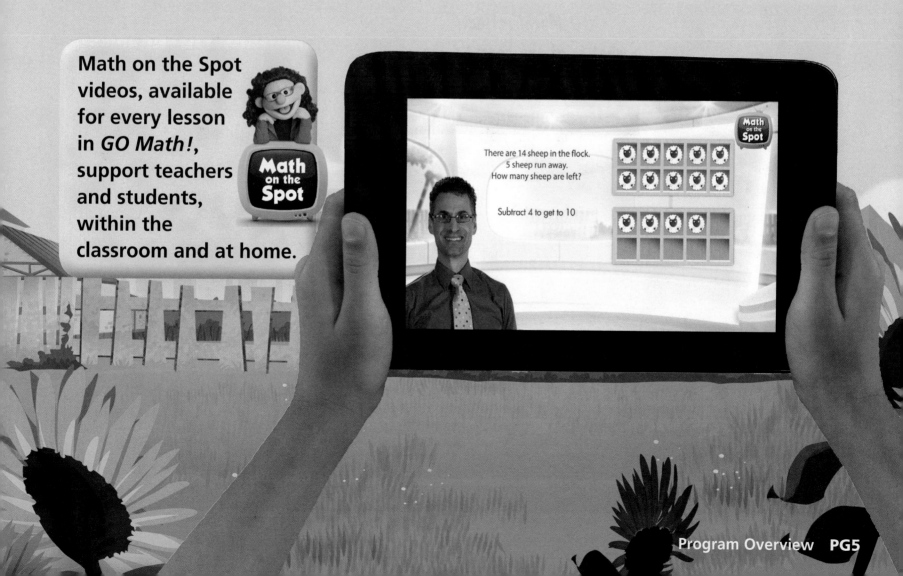

There are 14 sheep in the flock.
5 sheep run away.
How many sheep are left?

Subtract 4 to get to 10

A way of thinking about learning

GO Math! helps students engage with the standards and practices in new ways. Lessons begin with problem-based situations and then build to more abstract problems. All along the way, students use multiple models, manipulatives, quick pictures, and symbols to build mathematical understanding. Best of all, **GO Math!** is write-in at every grade level, so students are completely engaged.

GO Math! reflects what is at the heart of the Common Core Standards,

FOCUS   COHERENCE   RIGOR

that truly prepares students for the Common Core Assessments.

GO Math! works! Using manipulatives, multiple models, and rich, rigorous questions, students move through a carefully-sequenced arc of learning. They develop deep conceptual understanding, and then they practice, apply, and discuss what they know with skill and confidence. The equal emphases on understanding, procedural skills and fluency, and application help turn students into problem solvers and critical thinkers.

Digital resources to help personalize learning for students . . .

The Interactive Student Edition offers an alternate way to access grade-level content with audio, video, and animation. Our unique Personal Math Trainer® Powered by Knewton™ is embedded in the Interactive Student Edition to support students as they develop understanding. The Personal Math Trainer is a state-of-the-art, adaptive assessment and intervention system. In this tablet-based, mobile, and online environment, students receive a completely-personalized learning experience, focused on in-depth understanding, fluency, and application of standards.

and the HMH Player app to help teachers with planning, instruction, and collaboration.

With the HMH Player app, teachers and students can access the Interactive Student Edition while connected to the Internet from tablets, laptops, or desktop computers. They can download Personal Math Trainer assignments and content to their devices for offline access at any time. In addition, HMH Player includes powerful presentation tools for teachers and collaboration tools that keep teachers and students connected.

Create daily lesson plans with a single search.

Works in both online and offline environments.

Organize resources quickly.

See a snapshot of recent student report data.

Reports

8:42 AM

Class Assignments | Class Progress

Mr. Ryan's Class

Class Standards Progress

82%

Key
90%-100%
80%-89%
70%-79%
60%-69%
0%-59%

Student Name ▾	Average ▾
Grace, Emma	76%
Guerra, Devin	91%
Hannon, Erin	95%
Plato, Kacy	89%
Risner, Ellie	91%

84%
2.OA.C.3 National Common Core Math (2013)

90%
2.NBT.A.2 National Common Core Math (2013)

91%
2.NBT.A.3 National Common Core Math (2013)

81%
2.NBT.B.5 National Common Core Math (2013)

67%
2.NBT.B.6 National Common Core Math (2013)

Grab-and-Go Resources,

GO Math! works for the busy teacher. Everything from Teacher Editions to activity centers to manipulatives are organized in a ready-made, grab-and-go way to save you time.

GO Math! Teacher Editions are color-coded by Critical Area and organized by chapter to help teachers quickly identify materials and flexibly organize their curriculum. In addition, color coding is used to identify content as major, supporting, or additional work, providing teachers with a simple system to quickly identify and emphasize the most important grade-level material. The **GO Math!** classroom focuses on developing in-depth understanding and fosters communication within an engaging, inclusive environment.

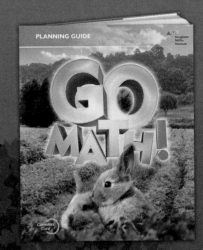

perfect for the busy teacher.

The Grab-and-Go Differentiated Centers Kits are ready-made differentiated math centers with activities, games, and literature. Resources for every lesson and special challenge materials make the Grab-and-Go Kits the perfect resource for independent practice.

Digital Resources

FOR LEARNING...

 ### Interactive Student Edition

- Immerses students in an interactive, multi-sensory math environment
- Enhances learning with scaffolded, interactive instruction and just-in-time feedback
- Provides audio reinforcement for each lesson
- Makes learning a two-way experience, using a variety of interactive tools

FOR ASSESSMENT AND INTERVENTION...

 ### Personal Math Trainer

- Creates a personalized learning path for each student
- Provides opportunities for practice, homework, and assessment
- Includes worked-out examples and helpful video support
- Offers targeted intervention and extra support to build proficiency and understanding

FOR DAILY MATH TUTORING...

 ### Math on the Spot Videos

- Models good problem-solving thinking in every lesson
- Engages students through interesting animations and fun characters
- Builds student problem-solving proficiency and confidence
- Builds the skills needed for success on the Common Core Assessments

FOR SIMPLICITY...

HMH Player App

It's For Students ...

• Content is available online, offline, and on-the-go!

• Students are engaged in class, at home, and anywhere in between for uninterrupted instruction

• Raise a Hand for instant student-teacher-student communication

... And For Teachers!

• Teachers can monitor student progress in real time

• Lesson customization features allow teachers to deliver personalized learning

• Plan your lessons, make assignments, and view results from the convenience of your classroom, at home, or on-the-go

• Supports blended learning through anywhere digital instruction

FOR TEACHING...

Digital Management System

• Manage online all program content and components

• Search for and select resources based on Common Core State Standards

• Identify resources based on student ability and needs

• View and assign student lessons, practice, assessments, and more

Professional Development Videos

• Learn more about the Common Core and Common Core content

• See first-hand the integration of the Mathematical Practices

• Watch students engaged in a productive struggle

Assessment ➡ Diagnosis ➡ Intervention

Data-Driven Decision Making

GO Math! allows for quick and accurate data-driven decision making so you can spend more instructional time tailored to children's needs.

Program Assessment Options with Intervention

Diagnostic

To allow children to be engaged from the beginning of the year

- **Prerequisite Skills Inventory** in *Chapter Resources*
- **Beginning-of-Year Test** in *Chapter Resources*
- **Show What You Know** in *Student Edition*

- Intensive Intervention
- Intensive Intervention User Guide
- Strategic Intervention
- Personal Math Trainer

Formative

To monitor children's understanding of lessons and to adjust instruction accordingly

- **Lesson Quick Check** in *Teacher Edition*
- **Lesson Practice** in *Student Edition*
- **Mid-Chapter Checkpoint** in *Student Edition*
- **Portfolio** in *Chapter Resources and Teacher Edition*
- **Middle-of-Year Test** in *Chapter Resources*

- **Reteach** with each lesson
- **RtI: Tier 1 and Tier 2 Activities** online
- Personal Math Trainer

Summative

To determine whether children have achieved the chapter objectives

- **Chapter Review/Test** in *Student Edition*
- **Chapter Test** in *Chapter Resources* (Common Core assessment format tests)
- **Performance Assessment Task** in *Chapter Resources*
- **End-of-Year Test** in *Chapter Resources*
- **Getting Ready for Grade 1 Test** in *Getting Ready Lessons and Resources*

- **Reteach** with each lesson
- **RtI: Tier 1 and Tier 2 Activities** online
- Personal Math Trainer

Tracking Yearly Progress

Beginning of the Year

The Beginning-of-Year Test determines how many of this year's Common Core standards students already understand. Adjust lesson pacing for skills that need light coverage and allow more time for skills students find challenging.

During the Year

Chapter Tests, Performance Assessments, and the Middle-of-Year Test monitor students' progress throughout the year. Plan time to reinforce skills students have not mastered.

End of the Year

The End-of-Year Test assesses students' mastery of this year's Common Core standards. Reinforce skills that students find challenging in order to provide the greatest possible success.

Performance Assessment

Performance Assessment helps to reveal the thinking strategies students use to solve problems. The Performance Tasks in *GO Math!* can be used to complete the picture for how students reason about mathematics.

GO Math! has a Performance Task for each Chapter and Critical Area. Each task has several parts that target specific math concepts, skills, and strategies. These tasks can help assess students' ability to use what they have learned to solve everyday problems. Teachers can plan for students to complete one task at a time or use an extended amount of time to complete the entire assessment. Projects for each Critical Area also serve to assess students' problem solving strategies and understanding of mathematical concepts they learn in the Critical Area.

Augmenting the Performance Tasks are a series of professional development videos featuring author Juli Dixon. Working with students, Juli models effective teaching and assessment practices. Additionally, each video provides insight into the dynamics of the classroom and how to use tasks not only to assess progress, but also to deepen understanding.

The Performance Tasks and Critical Area Projects offer the following features:

- They model good instruction.
- They are flexible.
- They are diagnostic.
- They use authentic instruction.
- They encourage the thinking process.
- They are scored holistically.

GO Math! Personal Math Trainer® Powered by Knewton™

- Online and adaptive homework, assessment, practice, and intervention engine
- Algorithmic, tech-enhanced items with wrong-answer feedback and learning aids
- Pre-built assignments that can generate personalized warm-ups, enrichment, or intervention

Authors

Edward B. Burger, Ph.D.
President, Southwestern University
Georgetown, Texas

Juli K. Dixon, Ph.D.
Professor, Mathematics Education
University of Central Florida
Orlando, Florida

Matthew R. Larson, Ph.D.
K-12 Curriculum Specialist for Mathematics
Lincoln Public Schools
Lincoln, Nebraska

Martha E. Sandoval-Martinez
Math Instructor
El Camino College
Torrance, California

Steven J. Leinwand
Principal Research Analyst
American Institutes for Research (AIR)
Washington, D.C.

Contributor and Consultant

Rena Petrello
Professor, Mathematics
Moorpark College
Moorpark, CA

Elizabeth Jiménez
CEO, GEMAS Consulting
Professional Expert on English Learner Education
Bilingual Education and Dual Language
Pomona, California

GO Math! Reviewers and Field Test Teachers

Janine L. Ambrose
Instructional Coach
Grades Taught: K–7
Sunset Ridge Elementary
Pendergast Elementary School District
Phoenix, Arizona

Patricia R. Barbour
Teacher: Grade 2
Sara Lindemuth Primary School
Susquehanna Township School District
Harrisburg, Pennsylvania

Pamela Bauer
Speech/Language Pathologist, M.A., CCC/SLP
Special School District of St. Louis County
Kindergarten Interventionist
Arrowpoint Elementary
Hazelwood, Missouri

James Brohn
Principal
Morning Star Lutheran School
Jackson, Wisconsin

Earl S. Brown
Teacher: Middle School Math
Susquehanna Township Middle School
Susquehanna Township School District
Harrisburg, Pennsylvania

Rebecca Centerino
Teacher: Grade 1
Zitzman Elementary
Meramec Valley RIII School District
Pacific, Missouri

Jessica Z. Jacobs
Assistant Principal
Thomas Holtzman Junior Elementary School
Susquehanna Township School District
Harrisburg, Pennsylvania

Tonya Leonard
Teacher: Grade 3
Peine Ridge Elementary
Wentzville RIV School District
Wentzville, Missouri

Jennifer Love Frier
Teacher: Grade 1
Olathe School District
Olathe, Kansas

Michelle Mieger
Teacher: Grade 3
Cedar Springs Elementary
Northwest R-1
House Springs, Missouri

Jeanne K. Selissen
Teacher: Grade 4
Tewksbury School District
Tewksbury, Massachusetts

Jo Ellen Showers
Teacher: Grade K
Sara Lindemuth Primary School
Susquehanna Township School District
Harrisburg, Pennsylvania

Judith M. Stagoski
Grades Taught: 5–8
District: Archdiocese of St. Louis
St. Louis, Missouri

Pauline Von Hoffer
Grades Taught: 4–12
Curriculum Coordinator
Wentzville School District
Wentzville, Missouri

Content Standards

PROFESSIONAL DEVELOPMENT · **by Matthew R. Larson, Ph.D.**
K-12 Curriculum Specialist for Mathematics
Lincoln Public Schools
Lincoln, Nebraska

Why Common Core State Standards for Mathematics?

The Common Core State Standards Initiative was a state-led process initiated by the Council of Chief State School Officers (CCSSO) and The National Governors Association (NGA). The goal was to create a set of Career and College Readiness Standards in mathematics (and English/Language Arts) so that all students graduate from high school ready for college and/or work. The K–8 standards outline a grade-by-grade roadmap to prepare students for the Career and College Readiness Standards.

Two primary concerns motivated the Common Core State Standards Initiative. First, inconsistent curricular standards, assessments, and proficiency cut scores across the 50 states raised equity issues (Reed, 2009). These different systems often led to wide disparities between student scores on state assessments in reading and math compared to student performance on the National Assessment of Educational Progress (Schneider, 2007). Second, U.S. students are not leaving school with skills necessary for success in college or the workforce. Results of international assessments, including *PISA* (Baldi, Jin, Skemer, Green, & Herget, 2007) and *TIMSS* (Gonzales, Williams, Jocelyn, Roey, Kastberg, & Brenwald, 2008) indicate that U.S. students do not achieve in mathematics at the level of students in other countries. This raises concern about U.S. economic competitiveness in an environment where U.S. students compete with students all across the globe.

Organization of the Common Core State Standards for Mathematics

The *Common Core State Standards for Mathematics* are organized into content standards and standards for mathematical practice. The content standards are addressed in this article.

The content standards have three levels of organization. The standards define what students should understand and be able to do. These standards are organized into clusters of related standards to emphasize mathematical connections. Finally, domains represent larger groups of related standards. The development and grade placement of standards considered research-based learning progressions with respect to how students' mathematical knowledge develops over time. At the elementary (K–6) level, there are ten content domains. Each grade addresses four or five domains.

Domain	Grade Level
Counting and Cardinality	K
Operations and Algebraic Thinking	K, 1, 2, 3, 4, 5
Number and Operations in Base Ten	K, 1, 2, 3, 4, 5
Measurement and Data	K, 1, 2, 3, 4, 5
Geometry	K, 1, 2, 3, 4, 5, 6
Number and Operations—Fractions	3, 4, 5
Ratios and Proportional Relationships	6
The Number System	6
Expressions and Equations	6
Statistics and Probability	6

Within each grade, each cluster (and the standards within each cluster) is considered to represent the major work of the grade, supplemental work, or additional work. Within the *Planning and Pacing Guide Instructional Path* in this *Planning Guide*, each lesson is color-coded to indicate whether the lesson is addressing the major work, the content that is supplemental, or the content that is additional.

While the total number of standards in the *Common Core* is generally less than the number of standards in many current state standard documents (NCTM, 2005; Reys, Chval, Dingman, McNaught, Regis, & Togashi, 2007), the emphasis in the *Common Core* is not simply on a list with fewer standards, but on a list that is also more specific and clear.

Note: This article references *Common Core State Standards for Mathematics*. © Copyright 2010.
National Governors Association Center for Best Practices and Council of Chief State School Officers. All rights reserved.

Critical Areas

The *Common Core* also specifies critical areas for instructional emphasis at each grade level. These areas are shown below.

K	• Representing, relating, and operating on whole numbers initially with sets of objects • Describing shapes and space
1	• Developing understanding of addition, subtraction, and strategies for addition and subtraction within 20 • Developing understanding of whole number relationships and place value, including grouping in tens and ones • Developing understanding of linear measurement and measuring lengths as iterating length units • Reasoning about attributes of, and composing and decomposing geometric shapes
2	• Extending understanding of base-ten notation • Building fluency with addition and subtraction • Using standard units of measure • Describing and analyzing shapes
3	• Developing understanding of multiplication and division and strategies for multiplication and division within 100 • Developing understanding of fractions, especially unit fractions • Developing understanding of the structure of rectangular arrays and of area • Describing and analyzing two-dimensional shapes
4	• Developing understanding and fluency with multi-digit multiplication, and developing understanding of dividing to find quotients involving multi-digit dividends • Developing an understanding of fraction equivalence, addition and subtraction of fractions with like denominators, and multiplication of fractions by whole numbers • Understanding that geometric figures can be analyzed and classified based on their properties, such as having parallel sides, perpendicular sides, particular angle measures, and symmetry
5	• Developing fluency with addition and subtraction of fractions, and developing understanding of the multiplication of fractions and of division of fractions in limited cases (unit fractions divided by whole numbers and whole numbers divided by unit fractions) • Extending division to 2-digit divisors, integrating decimal fractions into the place value system and developing understanding of operations with decimals to hundredths, and developing fluency with whole number and decimal operations • Developing understanding of volume.
6	• Connecting ratio and rate to whole number multiplication and division and using concepts of ratio and rate to solve problems • Completing understanding of division of fractions and extending the notion of number to the system of rational numbers, which includes negative numbers • Writing, interpreting, and using expressions and equations • Developing understanding of statistical thinking

This design permits instruction in each grade to focus on fewer concepts and skills in greater depth, while simultaneously building a foundation for the next grade. For example, in the *Common Core,* fractions are not a significant focus of the curriculum until third grade; although, students decompose two-dimensional figures in previous grades to develop a foundation for fractions in third grade. Similarly, probability is delayed until the middle grades in the *Common Core.*

The *Common Core* states that "mathematical understanding and procedural skill are equally important," but stresses conceptual understanding of key ideas and organizing principles, to structure essential big ideas. Similar to other recent recommendations (NCTM, 2000; NMAP, 2008), this emphasis on conceptual understanding and procedural skill, along with the standards for mathematical practice calls for a balanced approach to mathematics instruction and the curriculum.

Common Core State Standards for Mathematics and *GO Math!*

Nearly all content standards today, whether articulated by a state, NCTM, or the *Common Core,* share one thing in common: they call for a more focused and coherent curriculum that treats topics in a manner that will enable students to develop deep understanding of the content. *GO Math!* espouses this emphasis on a focused and coherent curriculum that teaches for depth of understanding to help students learn.

All standards documents share one additional feature: alone they are not enough to ensure that students

achieve at higher levels (Fuhrman, Resnick, & Shepard, 2009). In *GO Math!,* the *Common Core State Standards* are merely the starting point. *GO Math!* represents a comprehensive system of mathematics instruction that provides teachers the tools they need to help students succeed with more focused and rigorous mathematics standards. Research-based *GO Math!* includes multiple instructional approaches, diagnostic assessments linked to differentiated instructional resources and tiered interventions, along with technology solutions to support and motivate students.

Standards for Mathematical Practice

PROFESSIONAL DEVELOPMENT

by **Juli K. Dixon, Ph.D.**
Professor, Mathematics Education
University of Central Florida
Orlando, Florida

Developing Processes and Proficiencies in Mathematics Learners

There are eight mathematical practices. They are based on the National Council of Teachers of Mathematics' (NCTM) Process Standards (NCTM, 2000) and the National Research Council's (NRC) Strands of Mathematical Proficiency (NRC, 2001).

It is likely that good teachers can find evidence of each of these standards for mathematical practice in their current teaching. Regardless, it is useful to examine them and think about how each contributes to the development of mathematically proficient students.

Throughout *GO Math!*, the Mathematical Practices incorporated within a lesson are identified in the Student Edition and the Teacher Edition. In some instances, a lesson will focus on a part of a practice—this approach will break apart the standard in such a way as to support in-depth understanding of the practice and over time will aid students in attending to the full meaning of the practice.

What follows is a description of how they might look in an elementary school classroom. Each of these examples is reflective of experiences supported by *GO Math!*

GO Math! supports the Standards for Mathematical Practice through several specific features including:

- Lessons focused on depth of content knowledge
- Unlock the Problem sections to begin lessons
- Math Talk questions prompting students to use varied strategies and to explain their reasoning
- Explicit use of specific practices within a lesson, with accompanying point-of-use teacher support
- Support for manipulative use and drawings directly on the student pages
- Prompts that lead students to write their own problems or to determine if the reasoning of others is reasonable
- Real-world problems that encourage students to develop productive dispositions

Practice 1: Make sense of problems and persevere in solving them.

This practice brings to mind developing a productive disposition as described in *Adding It Up* (NRC, 2001). In order for students to develop the diligence intended with this practice, they must be provided with problems for which a pathway toward a solution is not immediately evident. If students are asked to determine how much of a cookie each person would receive if 4 cookies were shared among 5 people, a solution pathway is evident if students understand fractions. The students could simply divide each cookie into five equal pieces and give each person one fifth of each cookie or $\frac{4}{5}$ of a cookie in all. Now, consider the same problem given the constraint that the first three cookies are each broken into two equal pieces to start and each person is given half of a cookie.

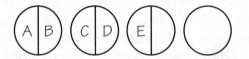

The problem is now more interesting and challenging. How will the remaining pieces of cookies be distributed among the five people? How will the students determine how much of a cookie each person has in all when all the cookies are shared? The students will likely refer back to the context of the problem to make sense of how to solve it, they will also very likely use pictures in their solution process. A solution is within reach but it will require diligence to persevere in reaching it.

Note: This article references *Common Core State Standards for Mathematics.* © Copyright 2010.
National Governors Association Center for Best Practices and Council of Chief State School Officers. All rights reserved.

© Houghton Mifflin Harcourt Publishing Company • Image Credits: (bg) ©maxstock/Alamy Images

Practice 2: Reason abstractly and quantitatively.

Story problems provide important opportunities for young learners to make sense of mathematics around them. Students often use strategies including acting out the problem to make sense of a solution path. Another important strategy is for students to make sense of the problem situation by determining a number sentence that could represent the problem and then solving it in a mathematically proficient way. Consider the following problem: *Jessica has 7 key chains in her collection. How many more does she need to have 15 key chains altogether?*

A child is presented with this problem, but rather than focusing on key words, the child uses the story to make sense of a solution process. The child knows to start with 7 then add something to that to get 15. The child represents this story abstractly by writing $7 + \_\_\_ = 15$. Then the child reasons quantitatively by thinking $7 + 3 = 10$ and $10 + 5 = 15$, so $7 + 8$ must equal 15 (because 3 and 5 are 8). The child then returns to the problem to see if a solution of 8 key chains makes sense. In doing so, the child makes "sense of quantities and their relationships in problem situations" (NGA Center/CCSSO, 2010, p. 6).

Practice 3: Construct viable arguments and critique the reasoning of others.

Students need to explain and justify their solution strategies. They should also listen to the explanations of other students and try to make sense of them. They will then be able to incorporate the reasoning of others into their own strategies and improve upon their own solutions. An example of this follows.

A group of students explores formulas for areas of quadrilaterals. Students make sense of the formula for the area of a parallelogram as $b \times h$ by decomposing parallelograms and composing a rectangle with the same area. Following this exploration, a student conjectures that the formula for the area of the trapezoid is also $b \times h$. The student draws this picture and says that the trapezoid can be "turned into" a rectangle with the same base by "moving one triangle over to the other side."

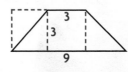

This student has constructed a viable argument based on a special type of trapezoid. Another student agrees that this formula works for an isosceles trapezoid

but asks if it will also work for a general trapezoid. This second student has made sense of the reasoning of the first student and asked a question to help improve the argument.

Practice 4: Model with mathematics.

Children need opportunities to use mathematics to solve real-world problems. As students learn more mathematics, the ways they model situations with mathematics should become more efficient. Consider the problem: *Riley has 4 blue erasers, Alex has 4 yellow erasers, and Paige has 4 purple erasers. How many erasers do they have in all?* A young child would likely model this problem with $4 + 4 + 4$. However, a mathematically proficient student in third grade should model the same situation with 3×4. This demonstrates how modeling will evolve through a child's experiences in mathematics and will change as their understanding grows.

A useful strategy for making sense of mathematics is for students to develop real-life contexts to correspond to mathematical expressions. This supports the reflexive relationship that if a student can write a word problem for a given expression, then the student can model a similar word problem with mathematics. Consider $\frac{4}{5} - \frac{1}{2}$. If a student is able to create a word problem to support this fraction subtraction, then, given a word problem, the student is more likely to be able to model the word problem with mathematics and solve it.

Practice 5: Use appropriate tools strategically.

At first glance, one might think that this practice refers to technological tools exclusively, however, tools also include paper and pencil, number lines and manipulatives (or concrete models). Mathematically proficient students are able to determine which tool to use for a given task. An example to illustrate this practice involves multiplying fractions. A student might choose to use a number line for one problem and paper and pencil procedures for another. If presented the problem $\frac{1}{3} \times \frac{3}{4}$, a mathematically proficient student might draw a number line and divide the distance from 0 to 1 into 4 equal parts drawing a darker line through the first three fourths. That student would see that $\frac{1}{3}$ of the $\frac{3}{4}$ is $\frac{1}{4}$ of the whole.

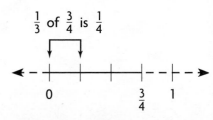

However, the same student presented with the problem $\frac{1}{3} \times \frac{4}{7}$ might not use a drawing at all but might find it more efficient to multiply the numerators and the denominators of the factors to get $\frac{4}{21}$ as the product. Both solution paths illustrate strategic use of tools for the given problems.

Practice 6: Attend to precision.

An important aspect of precision in mathematics is developed through the language used to describe it. This can be illustrated with definitions of geometric shapes. A kindergarten child is not expected to classify quadrilaterals. However, it is appropriate for a kindergarten child to name and describe shapes including squares and rectangles. Teachers seeking to support kindergarten children to attend to precision will include squares within sets of other rectangles so that these children will not use the language that all rectangles have two long sides and two short sides. These same students will be more likely to be able to correctly classify squares and rectangles in third grade because of this attention to precision when they are in kindergarten.

Practice 7: Look for and make use of structure.

Students who have made sense of strategies based on properties for finding products of single digit factors (basic facts) will be more likely to apply those properties when exploring multidigit multiplication. Consider the importance of the distributive property in looking for and making use of structure in this case. A student who has made sense of 6×7 by solving 6×5 and 6×2 has used a strategy based on the distributive property where 6×7 can be thought of as $6 \times (5 + 2)$ and then the 6 can be "distributed over" the 5 and 2. This same student can apply the distributive property to make sense of 12×24 by thinking of 24 as $20 + 4$ and solving $12 \times 20 + 12 \times 4$. A student who can make sense of multidigit multiplication in this way is on a good path to making sense of the structure of the standard algorithm for multidigit multiplication.

Practice 8: Look for and express regularity in repeated reasoning.

Whether performing simple calculations or solving complex problems, students should take advantage of the regularity of mathematics. If students who are exploring the volume of right rectangular prisms are given centimeter cubes and grid paper, they can build a prism with a given base and explore how the volume changes as the height of the prism increases. Students who look for ways to describe the change should see that the height of the prism is a factor of the volume of the prism and that if the area of the base is known, the volume of the prism is determined by multiplying the area of the base by the height of the prism. Identifying this pattern and repeated reasoning will help students build an understanding of the formula for the volume of right rectangular prisms.

As evidenced by the examples of mathematical practices in elementary school classrooms, "a lack of understanding effectively prevents a student from engaging in the mathematical practices" (NGA Center/CCSSO, 2010, p. 8). Teachers address this challenge by focusing on mathematical practices while developing an understanding of the content they support. In so doing, this process facilitates the development of mathematically proficient students.

Supporting Mathematical Practices Through Questioning

When you ask...	*Students...*
• What is the problem asking? • How will you use that information? • What other information do you need? • Why did you choose that operation? • What is another way to solve that problem? • What did you do first? Why? • What can you do if you don't know how to solve a problem? • Have you solved a problem similar to this one? • When did you realize your first method would not work for this problem? • How do you know your answer makes sense?	**MP1** Make sense of problems and persevere in solving them.
• What is a situation that could be represented by this equation? • What operation did you use to represent the situation? • Why does that operation represent the situation? • What properties did you use to find the answer? • How do you know your answer is reasonable?	**MP2** Reason abstractly and quantitatively.
• Will that method always work? • How do you know? • What do you think about what she said? • Who can tell us about a different method? • What do you think will happen if...? • When would that not be true? • Why do you agree/disagree with what he said? • What do you want to ask her about that method? • How does that drawing support your work?	**MP3** Construct viable arguments and critique the reasoning of others.
• Why is that a good model for this problem? • How can you use a simpler problem to help you find the answer? • What conclusions can you make from your model? • How would you change your model if...?	**MP4** Model with mathematics.
• What could you use to help you solve the problem? • What strategy could you use to make that calculation easier? • How would estimation help you solve that problem? • Why did you decide to use...?	**MP5** Use appropriate tools strategically.
• How do you know your answer is reasonable? • How can you use math vocabulary in your explanation? • How do you know those answers are equivalent? • What does that mean?	**MP6** Attend to precision.
• How did you discover that pattern? • What other patterns can you find? • What rule did you use to make this group? • Why can you use that property in this problem? • How is that like...?	**MP7** Look for and make use of structure.
• What do you remember about...? • What happens when...? • What if you... instead of...? • What might be a shortcut for...?	**MP8** Look for and express regularity in repeated reasoning.

For the full text of the Standards for Mathematical Practices, see *Mathematical Practices in GO Math!* in the *Planning Guide*.

Mathematical Practices	Throughout *GO Math!* Look for...	Explanation
1. Make sense of problems and persevere in solving them. Mathematically proficient students start by explaining to themselves the meaning of a problem and looking for entry points to its solution. They analyze givens, constraints, relationships, and goals. They make conjectures about the form and meaning of the solution and plan a solution pathway rather than simply jumping into a solution attempt. They consider analogous problems, and try special cases and simpler forms of the original problem in order to gain insight into its solution. They monitor and evaluate their progress and change course if necessary. Older students might, depending on the context of the problem, transform algebraic expressions or change the viewing window on their graphing calculator to get the information they need. Mathematically proficient students can explain correspondences between equations, verbal descriptions, tables, and graphs or draw diagrams of important features and relationships, graph data, and search for regularity or trends. Younger students might rely on using concrete objects or pictures to help conceptualize and solve a problem. Mathematically proficient students check their answers to problems using a different method, and they continually ask themselves, "Does this make sense?" They can understand the approaches of others to solving complex problems and identify correspondences between different approaches.	**Some Examples:** **Problem Solving Lessons** Grade K, Lesson 1.9 Grade 1, Lesson 8.8 Grade 2, Lesson 1.7 **Unlock the Problem** Grade K, Lesson 2.4 Grade 1, Lesson 3.12 Grade 2, Lesson 6.6 **Try Another Problem** Grade K, Lesson 7.6 Grade 1, Lesson 8.8 Grade 2, Lesson 2.11 **Share and Show** Grade 1, Lesson 4.6 Grade 2, Lesson 9.4 **On Your Own** Grade K, Lesson 4.5 Grade 1, Lesson 6.8 Grade 2, Lesson 6.6	**Children learn to:** • analyze a problem. • explain what information they need to find to solve the problem. • determine what information they need to use to solve the problem. • develop a plan for solving the problem. • use concrete objects to conceptualize a problem. • draw quick pictures on MathBoards to help solve problems. • evaluate the solution for reasonableness. **Children learn to:** • look at similar problems and apply techniques used in the original problem to gain insight into the solution of a new problem. • draw quick pictures on MathBoards to help solve problems. • evaluate the solution for reasonableness. • persevere in solving a problem, determining what methods and strategies they have learned that they can apply to solve the problem.

Teacher Edition   Student Edition

Mathematical Practices	Throughout *GO Math!* Look for...	Explanation
2. **Reason abstractly and quantitatively.** Mathematically proficient students make sense of quantities and their relationships in problem situations. They bring two complementary abilities to bear on problems involving quantitative relationships: the ability to *decontextualize*—to abstract a given situation and represent it symbolically and manipulate the representing symbols as if they have a life of their own, without necessarily attending to their referents—and the ability to *contextualize*, to pause as needed during the manipulation process in order to probe into the referents for the symbols involved. Quantitative reasoning entails habits of creating a coherent representation of the problem at hand; considering the units involved; attending to the meaning of quantities, not just how to compute them; and knowing and flexibly using different properties of operations and objects.	**Some Examples:** **Model and Draw** Grade K, Lesson 5.4 Grade 1, Lesson 2.3 Grade 2, Lesson 3.9	**Children learn to:** • abstract a real-world situation and represent it symbolically as a number sentence as a way of solving a problem. • put the numbers and symbols in a number sentence back into the context of the real-world situation for the solution.
	Measurement and Geometry Lessons Grade K, Lesson 9.4 Grade 1, Lesson 11.2 Grade 2, Lesson 8.1	**Children learn to:** • focus on the meaning of quantities in measurement and geometry problems. • choose the most appropriate kind of unit to use to solve a problem.
	Lessons on the properties of operations Grade K, Lesson 5.8 Grade 1, Lesson 3.10 Grade 2, Lesson 3.2	**Children learn to use these properties of operations:** • changing the way addends are grouped in an addition problem does not change the sum. • changing the order of the addends in an addition problem does not change the sum.
	Lessons on modeling with manipulatives and drawings Grade K, Lesson 5.4 Grade 1, Lesson 5.1 Grade 2, Lesson 3.8	**Children learn to:** • represent real-world situations with concrete and pictorial models. • use bar models as one way to visualize addition and subtraction problems symbolically.

Teacher Edition **Student Edition**

Mathematical Practices	Throughout *GO Math!* Look for...	Explanation
3. Construct viable arguments and critique the reasoning of others. Mathematically proficient students understand and use stated assumptions, definitions, and previously established results in constructing arguments. They make conjectures and build a logical progression of statements to explore the truth of their conjectures. They are able to analyze situations by breaking them into cases, and can recognize and use counterexamples. They justify their conclusions, communicate them to others, and respond to the arguments of others. They reason inductively about data, making plausible arguments that take into account the context from which the data arose. Mathematically proficient students are also able to compare the effectiveness of two plausible arguments, distinguish correct logic or reasoning from that which is flawed, and—if there is a flaw in an argument—explain what it is. Elementary students can construct arguments using concrete referents such as objects, drawings, diagrams, and actions. Such arguments can make sense and be correct, even though they are not generalized or made formal until later grades. Later, students learn to determine domains to which an argument applies. Students at all grades can listen or read the arguments of others, decide whether they make sense, and ask useful questions to clarify or improve the arguments.	**Some Examples:** **Math Talk** Grade 1, Lesson 8.1 Grade 2, Lesson 10.5	**Children learn to:** • use mathematical language. • explain mathematical concepts. • defend, justify, or disprove a mathematical conjecture. • use deductive reasoning, definitions, and previously proven conclusions.
	Vocabulary Builder Grade K Grade 1 Grade 2 **Developing Math Language** Grade K Grade 1 Grade 2 **Vocabulary Preview** Grade 1 Grade 2	**Children learn to:** • develop, build, and reinforce mathematics vocabulary. • discuss mathematical definitions. • strengthen their abilities to communicate ideas about mathematics.
	Think Smarter Problems Grade K, Lesson 5.5 Grade 1, Lessons 2.9, 10.4 Grade 2, Lessons 6.8, 9.3 **Go Deeper** Grade K, Lesson 5.12 Grade 1, Lesson 6.3 Grade 2, Lessons 4.6, 5.2	**Children learn to:** • extend their thinking. • discuss their explanations. • give concrete examples to justify their explanations. • explain and describe mathematical understanding.

Teacher Edition   Student Edition

© Houghton Mifflin Harcourt Publishing Company • Image Credits: (bg) ©maxstock/Alamy Images

Mathematical Practices	Throughout *GO Math!* Look for...	Explanation
4. Model with mathematics. Mathematically proficient students can apply the mathematics they know to solve problems arising in everyday life, society, and the workplace. In early grades, this might be as simple as writing an addition equation to describe a situation. In middle grades, a student might apply proportional reasoning to plan a school event or analyze a problem in the community. By high school, a student might use geometry to solve a design problem or use a function to describe how one quantity of interest depends on another. Mathematically proficient students who can apply what they know are comfortable making assumptions and approximations to simplify a complicated situation, realizing that these may need revision later. They are able to identify important quantities in a practical situation and map their relationships using such tools as diagrams, two-way tables, graphs, flowcharts and formulas. They can analyze those relationships mathematically to draw conclusions. They routinely interpret their mathematical results in the context of the situation and reflect on whether the results make sense, possibly improving the model if it has not served its purpose.	**Some Examples:** **Unlock the Problem • Real World** Grade K, Lesson 6.3 Grade 1, Lessons 3.12, 10.7 Grade 2, Lesson 8.5	**Children learn to:** • apply the mathematics they know to solve real-world problems. • write a number sentence to describe a situation. • use diagrams, tables, and graphs to help them see relationships and draw conclusions in problems.
	Hands On Lessons Grade K, Lesson 6.4 Grade 1, Lesson 2.8 Grade 2, Lesson 7.4	**Children learn to:** • model in a 'hands-on' approach to analyze problems.
	Connect To... Cross-Curricular Grade K Grade 1 Grade 2 **Literature** Grade K Grade 1 Grade 2	**Children learn to:** • apply the mathematics they know to solve problems in Literature, Science, Social Studies, Art, and other disciplines. • appreciate how mathematics influences their lives in ways both large and small.

Teacher Edition   Student Edition

Mathematical Practices	Throughout GO Math! Look for...	Explanation
5. Use appropriate tools strategically. Mathematically proficient students consider the available tools when solving a mathematical problem. These tools might include pencil and paper, concrete models, a ruler, a protractor, a calculator, a spreadsheet, a computer algebra system, a statistical package, or dynamic geometry software. Proficient students are sufficiently familiar with tools appropriate for their grade or course to make sound decisions about when each of these tools might be helpful, recognizing both the insight to be gained and their limitations. For example, mathematically proficient high school students analyze graphs of functions and solutions generated using a graphing calculator. They detect possible errors by strategically using estimation and other mathematical knowledge. When making mathematical models, they know that technology can enable them to visualize the results of varying assumptions, explore consequences, and compare predictions with data. Mathematically proficient students at various grade levels are able to identify relevant external mathematical resources, such as digital content located on a website, and use them to pose or solve problems. They are able to use technological tools to explore and deepen their understanding of concepts.	**Some Examples:** **Hands-On Lessons** Grade K, Lesson 3.1 Grade 1, Lesson 12.3 Grade 2, Lesson 8.1	**Children learn to:** • use available tools to analyze problems through a concrete 'hands-on' approach.
	Geometry and Measurement Lessons Grade K, Lesson 10.7 Grade 1, Lesson 9.4 Grade 2, Lesson 11.7	**Children learn to use appropriate tools to:** • enhance and deepen their understanding of measurement and geometry concepts.
	Digital Path *i*Tools **Animated Math Models HMH Mega Math** All student lessons	**Children learn to use technological tools to:** • enhance and deepen their understanding of concepts. • enable them to visualize problems. • explore consequences of varying the data given.
6. Attend to precision. Mathematically proficient students try to communicate precisely to others. They try to use clear definitions in discussion with others and in their own reasoning. They state the meaning of the symbols they choose, including using the equal sign consistently and appropriately. They are careful about specifying units of measure, and labeling axes to clarify the correspondence with quantities in a problem. They calculate accurately and efficiently, express numerical answers with a degree of precision appropriate for the problem context. In the elementary grades, students give carefully formulated explanations to each other. By the time they reach high school they have learned to examine claims and make explicit use of definitions.	**Math Talk** Grade 1, Lesson 12.1 Grade 2, Lesson 5.4	**Children learn to:** • communicate precisely. • use mathematical vocabulary to communicate their ideas and explanations and to justify their thinking and solutions.
	Skill Lessons on number sentences and comparisons Grade K, Lesson 5.7 Grade 1, Lessons 7.3, 7.4 Grade 2, Lesson 2.12	**Children learn to:** • state the meaning of the symbols $(+, -, <, >, =)$ they use in mathematical expressions and sentences accurately. • use the equal sign appropriately. • calculate accurately. • use comparison symbols $(<, >)$ appropriately.
	Measurement Lessons Grade 1, Lesson 9.3 Grade 2, Lesson 8.6	**Children learn to:** • use correct measurement units for solutions.

Teacher Edition   Student Edition

© Houghton Mifflin Harcourt Publishing Company • Image Credits: (bg) ©maxstock/Alamy Images

Mathematical Practices	Throughout *GO Math!* Look for...	Explanation
7. **Look for and make use of structure.** Mathematically proficient students look closely to discern a pattern or structure. Young students, for example, might notice that three and seven more is the same amount as seven and three more, or they may sort a collection of shapes according to how many sides the shapes have. Later, students will see 7×8 equals the well remembered $7 \times 5 + 7 \times 3$, in preparation for learning about the distributive property. In the expression $x^2 + 9x + 14$, older students can see the 14 as 2×7 and the 9 as $2 + 7$. They recognize the significance of an existing line in a geometric figure and can use the strategy of drawing an auxiliary line for solving problems. They also can step back for an overview and shift perspective. They can see complicated things, such as some algebraic expressions, as single objects or as being composed of several objects. For example, they can see $5 - 3(x - y)^2$ as 5 minus a positive number times a square and use that to realize that its value cannot be more than 5 for any real numbers x and y.	**Some Examples:** **Lessons with patterns** Grade K, Lesson 9.11 Grade 1, Lesson 6.1 Grade 2, Lesson 1.9	**Children learn to:** • sort shapes according to attributes. • use mathematical vocabulary to communicate their ideas and explanations and to justify their thinking and solutions. • use familiar patterns in our number system to extend counting sequences.
	Geometry Lessons Grade 1, Lessons 11.4, 12.1 Grade 2, Lesson 11.3	**Children learn to:** • verify that a new three-dimensional shape can be composed by combining three-dimensional shapes. • recognize and identify shapes by the number of side and vertices. • apply the structure of the base-ten number system to deeper understanding of the values of multi-digit numbers.
	Lessons with basic facts Grade 1, Lessons 3.1, 3.6 Grade 2, Lesson 3.7	**Children learn to:** • use a variety of different strategies to find the sums and differences of basic facts. • use benchmark number 10 when finding differences.
8. **Look for and express regularity in repeated reasoning.** Mathematically proficient students notice if calculations are repeated, and look both for general methods and for shortcuts. Upper elementary students might notice when dividing 25 by 11 that they are repeating the same calculations over and over again, and conclude they have a repeating decimal. By paying attention to the calculation of slope as they repeatedly check whether points are on the line through (1, 2) with slope 3, middle school students might abstract the equation $(y - 2)/(x - 1) = 3$. Noticing the regularity in the way terms cancel when expanding $(x - 1)(x + 1)$, $(x - 1)(x^2 + x + 1)$, and $(x - 1)(x^3 + x^2 + x + 1)$ might lead them to the general formula for the sum of a geometric series. As they work to solve a problem, mathematically proficient students maintain oversight of the process, while attending to the details. They continually evaluate the reasonableness of their intermediate results.	**Lessons with basic facts** Grade K, Lesson 6.7 Grade 1, Lessons 3.3, 5.5 Grade 2, Lesson 3.3	**Children learn to:** • find patterns in basic-fact strategies, such as the 'make a ten' 'doubles plus 1' and 'double minus 1'. • see the relationship between addition and subtraction. • recognize how structure and calculations are repeated as they build fact families. • discover shortcuts for finding sums of basic facts and for recognizing counting patterns.
	Multi-digit Computation Lessons Grade 1, Lesson 8.10 Grade 2, Lesson 6.7	**Children learn to:** • repeat the same steps for each place-value position in the standard algorithm for multi-digit computation.
	Lessons on Comparing Numbers Grade K, Lesson 4.7 Grade 1, Lesson 7.3 Grade 2, Lesson 2.12	**Children learn to:** • model and compare numbers to determine which is less or greater.

Teacher Edition   Student Edition

The Algebra Progression in *GO Math!* Grades K–8 and the GIMET-QR

PROFESSIONAL DEVELOPMENT

by Matthew R. Larson, Ph.D.
K–12 Curriculum Specialist for Mathematics
Lincoln Public Schools
Lincoln, Nebraska
NCTM President (2016–2018)

Nearly two decades ago, NCTM first articulated the need for algebra to be a significant strand across the K–8 curriculum in *Principles and Standards for School Mathematics* (NCTM, 2000). The importance of algebra in Grades K–8 was reemphasized in the final report of the National Mathematics Advisory Panel (NMAP, 2008). A coherent, rigorous, and sound learning progression in the K–8 mathematics curriculum is necessary to prepare students not only for high school mathematics courses, but also to ensure they leave high school both college and career ready.

The Grade-Level Instructional Materials Evaluation Tool—Quality Review (GIMET-QR) for Grades K–8 was developed to provide educators with a framework for evaluating the quality of instructional materials and choosing materials that are best suited to provide a coherent learning experience. This tool focuses on the clusters and standards along the progression to algebra continuum.

Using the progression documents from the University of Arizona Institute of Mathematics and the Progression to Algebra Continuum from the Common Core, the developers of GIMET-QR developed additional algebra-progression statements for each grade level. These particular statements provide additional specificity and clarity for the reviewers of instructional materials.

This article examines the Houghton Mifflin Harcourt *GO Math!* Grades K–8 program and the extent to which it reflects and embodies the GIMET-QR algebra-progression statements.

GO Math! Grades K–2

The GIMET-QR algebra-progression statements in this grade span draw from the Common Core domains Counting and Cardinality, Operations and Algebraic Thinking, Number and Operations in Base Ten, and Measurement and Data.

Based on the explanations, diagrams, pictorial representations, and assignments in the *GO Math!* instructional materials, and when considered in the context of the algebra-progression statements, *GO Math!* K–2 is exceptional in its comprehensive approach to algebra preparedness as defined by the GIMET-QR.

Kindergarten

In **Kindergarten**, students represent numbers in multiple ways, including with counters, drawings, and written numerals. Students show how to count objects arranged in lines and in more difficult arrangements. Teacher narrative ensures that students count each object only once and make single counting paths through scattered displays. The logical structure of *GO Math!* counting lessons supports students' understanding that each successive number name in a counting array refers to a quantity that is one greater. When students compare numbers, they do so in a variety of ways, including by using real objects, studying drawings, and counting. The assignments in the Student Edition support these comparisons as well. Lessons offer opportunities for students to match to compare numbers, and they show that one group might look like it has more objects, but matching or counting may yield another result.

It is significant that the Operations and Algebraic Thinking underpinnings for algebra in *GO Math!* at this grade span place notable emphasis on understanding written expressions and equations. Kindergarten students develop the mathematical language of addition and subtraction that is so integral to success with algebra. To solidify this development even more, addition and subtraction situations in *GO Math!* are action oriented, helping students to visualize and understand the change that takes place.

Finally, *GO Math!* Kindergarten is exceptional in its treatment of place value. Students have many hands-on opportunities to compose and decompose numbers as ten ones and some further ones, this concept being a critical step for understanding base-ten notation.

Grade 1

Students in **Grade 1** extend their understanding of algebra ideas in several ways. Students use comparison to represent problem situations, which requires students to conceptualize and represent an unknown. Mathematical language comes into play here as well. *More, fewer, or less* contextual problems can take many forms. *GO Math!* offers extensive opportunities to work toward mastery of the language and contextual complexities. Assignments require students to match objects with drawings and use labels to compare. Later, students use tape diagrams (bar models) as a tool to help them compare. Students represent *compare* situations in different ways, including as unknown-addend problems. Even though students do not use formal properties in their descriptions, they have many opportunities to recognize these properties in action.

In *GO Math!*, emphasis is placed through Math Talk structures on the explanation a student gives for his or her representation of a contextual situation. In *GO Math!* students gain extensive experience with more challenging problem subtypes as they begin developing an algebraic perspective on mathematical situations. *GO Math!* is exceptional in the ways it encourages students to link equations with representations, which leads to a deeper understanding of these precursors to formal algebra.

Here again, *GO Math!* excels in its teaching of place value. Instruction helps students recognize that the digit in the tens place is the critical digit when determining the size of a two-digit number. Assignments require students to explain why this is so. Students connect different strategies: for example, using the relationship between addition and subtraction to explain an unknown-addend problem.

In Grade 1, there are several GIMET-QR statements drawn from the Measurement and Data domain. These include transitive reasoning and the reasoning processes of seriation, conservation, and classification. Both the *GO Math!* recommended teacher instructional narrative and the assignments in the Student Edition emphasize these algebraic building blocks.

Grade 2

Grade 2 students extend their addition and subtraction representations to include two-step problems. *GO Math!* offers a recommended teacher narrative and assignments that engage students in representing two-step problems with equations by using easy subtypes. Students use drawings or combinations of drawings and equations to represent comparison problems or middle-difficulty subtypes. Assignments require students to solve one- and two-step problems that involve adding to, taking from, putting together/taking apart, and comparing and that have unknowns in all positions.

GO Math! offers the instruction and support students need to succeed when reading and writing equations with different placements of the unknown, explaining the different meanings of addition and subtraction, and showing the connection between addition and subtraction equations. Students develop and use mathematical language to explain their reasoning about *result unknown, change unknown,* and *start unknown* and the relationship between the three.

In Grade 2, there is further evidence of exceptional instruction and practice involving place value. Students are required to indicate the place value of three-digit numbers, determine the value of each digit, make connections between representations of three-digit numbers, and connect number words and numbers written in base-ten numerals as sums of their base-ten units, as well as to say the number aloud. *GO Math!* students successfully extend their understanding of place value to hundreds, which lays the foundation for base-ten structural work in later grades. Assignments help students understand that a hundred is a unit of 100 ones, and that both tens and hundreds can be composed or decomposed. Using mental math, *GO Math!* students develop the academic language required to use place value and properties of operations to explain why addition and subtraction strategies work.

GO Math! materials offer hands-on instruction and practice with measuring tools so that students understand that *one* represents a length beginning at the zero mark on a ruler and ending at 1, not the number 1 itself. The inverse relationship between the size of a unit of length and the number of units required to measure a length are well illustrated and explained.

GO Math! Grades 3–5

The GIMET-QR algebra-progression statements in the 3–5 elementary grade span are drawn from the Operations and Algebraic Thinking, Number and Operations in Base Ten, Number and Operations—Fractions, and Measurement and Data domains.

In the intermediate grades in *GO Math!*, the instruction, including the explanations and connections that foster the deep development of the concepts and skills that are part of the algebra progression in these grades, the Math Talk prompts that promote engagement and interaction between students and teacher as well as among students, and the assignments that cement the learning all fully support the algebra-progression statements in the GIMET-QR.

Grade 3

Grade 3 students in *GO Math!* have many meaningful opportunities to represent and solve contextual multiplication and division problems for unknown products, unknown group sizes, and unknown numbers of groups. Students illustrate equal groups and arrays/area representations, which lays the foundation for algebraic expressions. *GO Math!* emphasizes the academic language students need to explain their reasoning about unknown products, group sizes, and numbers of groups. Students understand that in equal groups, the roles of the factors differ. Assignments ensure that students are facile with columns and rows in arrays. Students manipulate rectangular arrays to visualize and more fully understand the Commutative Property of Multiplication. When solving for unknowns in problem situations, students make connections among problems, manipulate representations, and link equations to representations. Students build their algebraic perspective when making these connections. *GO Math!* assignments encourage students to model and apply the properties of multiplication and the relationship between multiplication and division by requiring them to illustrate the properties and relationship with drawings and equations; to make the connection that two factors are quotients of related division problems; and to relate the product, factors, or quotients to contextual problem situations.

GO Math! facilitates the development of fluency with multiplication and division by modeling decomposing and composing products that are known in order to find an unknown product. Assignments require students to explain the relationship between area and multiplication and addition, represent it in different ways, and then apply their understanding to problems involving multiplication and area.

GO Math! fully supports students' understanding of fractions as they move beyond the fraction language they learned in prior grades. Students partition a whole into equal parts and visualize unit fractions as the basic building blocks of fractions. Students use the number line to show that fractions are numbers and that unit fractions can be the measure of length. This extensive, hands-on work with fractions serves as a stepping stone from arithmetic to algebra and is consistent with the latest research on effective fraction instruction as outlined in the Institute of Education Sciences guide *Developing Effective Fractions Instruction for Kindergarten through 8th Grade* (Siegler et al., 2010) and NCTM's *Developing Essential Understanding of Rational Numbers for Teaching Mathematics in Grades 3–5* (Barnett-Clarke et al., 2010).

GO Math! materials help students conceptualize area as the amount of two-dimensional space in a bounded region and to measure it by choosing a unit of area. Students explain how they connect area to multiplication and addition. Assignments require students to determine the areas of rectilinear figures by composing and decomposing them into non-overlapping areas and adding the parts. This sophisticated way of finding area is applied to contextual problem situations.

Grade 4

In **Grade 4** multiplication and division, students focus on distinguishing multiplicative comparison from additive comparison. *GO Math!* instruction emphasizes that in an additive comparison, one asks what amount can be added to one quantity to result in the other; in multiplicative comparison, one asks what factor would multiply one quantity to result in another. The specificity and academic language for comparisons in *GO Math!* help prepare students for formal algebra and sophisticated courses in later years. Likewise, multistep contextual problems that require students to interpret remainders are assigned.

Just as in Grade 3, work with fractions is integral to building a solid foundation for formal algebra. In *GO Math!* Grade 4, students illustrate addition as putting together so that they understand the way fractions are built from unit fractions. Renaming a mixed number to a fraction is considered to be a case of fraction addition, whereas renaming an improper fraction as a mixed number is decomposition.

When comparing two decimals, *GO Math!* students use the meaning of decimals as fractions and make sure to compare fractions with the same denominator. This promotes a deeper understanding of rational numbers.

Grade 5

Grade 5 students in *GO Math!* explain how multiplying a number by a power of 10 "shifts" every digit to the left. They use place value to explain patterns in the number of zeroes in products of whole numbers, powers of 10 and exponents, and the location of the decimal point in products of decimals with powers of 10. Assignments require students to connect the academic language of multiples to powers in order to understand multiplication with exponentiation. Students explain patterns when multiplying whole numbers or decimals by powers of 10.

Work with fractions at this level involves multiplication and division. With *GO Math!* materials, students connect the interpretation of a fraction as division to an understanding of division as equal sharing. Students make the connection between fraction multiplication and finding the area of a rectangle.

With *GO Math!*, students interpret multiplication of fractions as scaling in several ways. Without multiplying, they compare the size of the product to the size of one factor on the basis of the size of the other factor. Students explain why multiplying a given number by a fraction greater than 1 results in a product greater than the given number. Likewise, they explain why multiplying a fraction by a fraction less than 1 results in a product less than the given number. *GO Math!* students view multiplication as an operation that "stretches or shrinks" by a scale factor, which leads them to reason multiplicatively with continuous quantities.

Grade 5 students find the volume of a solid figure composed of two non-overlapping right rectangular prisms by adding the volumes of the parts. In *GO Math!*, students use this method to complete a space architecture project and justify how their design meets the specific volume criterion.

GO Math! Grades 6–8

The GIMET-QR algebra-progression statements in the middle grades are drawn from the domains The Number System, Ratios and Proportional Relationships, and Expressions and Equations.

The *GO Math!* instructional models, materials, and assignments for this grade span make meaningful connections with the concepts and skills taught in prior years and fully prepare students for algebra courses and beyond in high school.

Grade 6

The **Grade 6** instruction and assignments in *GO Math!* provide many opportunities for students to use story contexts and visual models to develop and deepen their understanding of fraction division. These opportunities help connect the relation between multiplication and division to fraction division.

The number line is extended to include negative numbers so that students can investigate negative numbers in context when describing magnitude and direction. Students use the number line to compare numbers based on their relative positions rather than their magnitudes. To avoid confusion with distance from zero and absolute value, *GO Math!* provides students contextual problems where it makes sense to compare the relative positions of two rational numbers and to compare their absolute values, and to witness where these two comparisons run in different directions.

GO Math! instruction on the concepts of ratio and rate is focused on the proportional relationship between two quantities. *GO Math!* assignments require students to explain their solutions to ratio and rate-reasoning problems. To support their explanations, the materials provide instruction in the use of tables of equivalent ratios, tape diagrams (bar models), double-number line diagrams, and the unit rate a/b associated with a ratio $a:b$.

In Grade 6, students connect their previous understanding of arithmetic to algebraic expressions and equations. With *GO Math!*, students use mathematical terms to explain how one or more parts of an expression correspond to the quantities in a contextual problem. Students interpret the structure of an expression in terms of a context. Work with numerical expressions prepares students for work with algebraic expressions. *GO Math!* supports this transition by instructing students to leave numerical expressions unevaluated, which prepares students for constructing the algebraic equation to solve the problem.

GO Math! assignments require students to use the process of reasoning to find the number which makes an equation true. This process includes checking whether a given number is a solution. Students work toward finding a standard method for solving equations, but they begin by studying examples and looking for structure. Their study leads to understanding that every occurrence of a given variable has the same value throughout the solution procedure.

Students then show their understanding of quantitative relationships between dependent and independent variables. They analyze the relationship between the variables by using graphs and tables, and they explain how these relate to the equation. This work with two variables prepares students for later work with functions.

Grade 7

The **Grade 7** *GO Math!* materials define a proportional relationship and then use that definition to determine if a relationship is proportional. Students examine situations carefully to determine the existence of a proportional relationship. *GO Math!* emphasizes the importance of structure and language by prompting students to look for and understand the roles of the terms *for every, for each,* and *per.* Teachers are reminded of typical misconceptions involving proportional relationships and offered suggestions for how to avoid them. The program explains the correspondences between representations including tables, equations, graphs, diagrams, and verbal descriptions. Students are required to test for equivalent ratios by using a table or by graphing on a coordinate plane and to show

how the unit rate appears in each representation.

GO Math! students add and subtract rational numbers and represent the addition and subtraction on a horizontal or vertical number line. *GO Math!* materials demonstrate that each directed line segment has a direction, a beginning, and an end. When these directed line segments are linked, the second line segment begins at the end of the first one. Students realize that if the second line segment is going in the opposite direction to the first, then it can backtrack over the first and essentially cancel all or part of it out. This realization effectively lays the foundation for work with vectors in high school.

Students in *GO Math!* learn to simplify general linear expressions with rational coefficients. Students extend their prior understanding of order of operations and applied properties of operations to linear expressions that have more operations and whose transformations require an understanding of the rules for multiplying negative numbers. Here again, the *GO Math!* teacher notes identify typical student misconceptions in simplifying expressions and offer suggestions for addressing them.

Grade 8

In **Grade 8**, *GO Math!* students apply the properties of integer exponents to generate equivalent numerical expressions. Requiring the rule $10^a \cdot 10^b = 10^{a+b}$ to hold when a and b are integers leads to the definition of the meaning of powers with 0 and negative exponents. Students prepare for learning the properties of exponents in high school by working systematically with the square root and cube root symbols in *GO Math!* Assignments require students to express and perform calculations with very large or very small numbers by using scientific notation.

GO Math! materials illustrate the connections between proportional relationships, lines, and linear equations. Students start to build a unified notion of the concept of function, leading them to compare two different proportional relationships represented in different ways. Students understand that the connection between the unit rate in a proportional relationship and the slope of its graph depends on a connection with the geometry of similar triangles.

Students use a function to model a linear relationship between two quantities. They determine the rate of change, which is the slope of the line that is the graph of the function. Students read, compute, or approximate the rate of change from a table or graph. To foster understanding of relationships between quantities, *GO Math!* assignments ask students to describe the relationships quantitatively and to pay attention to the general shape of the graph without concern for the numerical values.

The *GO Math!* K–8 program presents a coherent algebra learning progression as illustrated by its content alignment to the GIMET-QR. Its comprehensive representation of the algebra progressions in its materials and assignments, combined with an instructional design that engages learners in developing not only procedural fluency, but deep conceptual understanding, is clear evidence that *GO Math!* is a high-quality mathematics program that fully prepares students for high school mathematics courses and beyond.

Bibliography

Barnett-Clarke, Carne, William Fisher, Rick Marks, and Sharon Ross. *Developing Essential Understanding of Rational Numbers for Teaching Mathematics in Grades 3–5*. Reston, VA: NCTM, 2010.

Council of the Great City Schools. Grade-Level Instructional Materials Evaluation Tool-Quality Review (GIMET-QR). Washington, DC: Council of the Great City Schools. http://www.cgcs.org/page/475

National Council of Teachers of Mathematics. *Principles and Standards for School Mathematics*. Edited by NCTM. Reston, VA: NCTM, 2000.

National Mathematics Advisory Panel. *Foundations for Success: The Final Report of the National Mathematics Advisory Panel*. Washington, DC: U.S. Department of Education, 2008.

"Progress to Algebra in Grades K–8." In "K–8 Publishers' Criteria for the Common Core State Standards for Mathematics," 8. 20 July 2012. http://www.corestandards.org/assets/Math_Publishers_Criteria_K-8_Summer%202012_FINAL.pdf

Siegler, Robert, Thomas Carpenter, Francis (Skip) Fennell, David Geary, James Lewis, Yukari Okamoto, Laurie Thompson, and Jonathan Wray, J. *Developing Effective Fractions Instruction for Kindergarten Through 8th Grade* (NCEE #2010-4039). Washington, DC: National Center for Education Evaluation and Regional Assistance, Institute of Education Sciences, U.S. Department of Education, 2010. Retrieved from whatworks.ed.gov/publications/practiceguides.

Progress to Algebra in Grades K–8

K	1	2	3	4
Know number names and the count sequence	Represent and solve problems involving addition and subtraction		Represent and solve problems involving multiplication and division	Use the four operations with whole numbers to solve problems
Count to tell the number of objects	Understand and apply properties of operations and the relationship between addition and subtraction	Represent and solve problems involving addition and subtraction	Understand properties of multiplication and the relationship between multiplication and division	Generalize place value understanding for multi-digit whole numbers
Compare numbers	Add and subtract within 20	Add and subtract within 20	Multiply and divide within 100	Use place value understanding and properties of operations to perform multi-digit arithmetic
Understand addition as putting together and adding to, and understand subtraction as taking apart and taking from	Work with addition and subtraction equations	Understand place value	Solve problems involving the four operations, and identify and explain patterns in arithmetic	Extend understanding of fraction equivalence and ordering
Work with numbers 11–19 to gain foundations for place value	Extend the counting sequence	Use place value understanding and properties of operations to add and subtract	Develop understanding of fractions as numbers	Build fractions from unit fractions by applying and extending previous understandings of operations
	Understand place value	Measure and estimate lengths in standard units	Solve problems involving measurement and estimation of intervals of time, liquid volumes, and masses of objects	Understand decimal notation for fractions, and compare decimal fractions
	Use place value understanding and properties of operations to add and subtract	Relate addition and subtraction to length		
	Measure lengths indirectly and by iterating length units		Geometric measurement: understand concepts of area and relate area to multiplication and to addition	

5	6	7	8
Understand the place value system	Apply and extend previous understandings of multiplication and division to divide fractions by fractions	Apply and extend previous understanding of operations with fractions to add, subtract, multiply, and divide rational numbers	Work with radical and integer exponents
Perform operations with multi-digit whole numbers and decimals to hundredths			
Use equivalent fractions as a strategy to add and subtract fractions	Apply and extend previous understandings of numbers to the system of rational numbers		Understand the connections between proportional relationships, lines, and linear equations
	Understand ratio concepts and use ratio reasoning to solve problems	Analyze proportional relationships and use them to solve real-world and mathematical problems	
Apply and extend previous understandings of multiplication and division to multiply and divide fractions			Analyze and solve linear equations and pairs of simultaneous linear equations
	Apply and extend previous understandings of arithmetic to algebraic expressions	Use properties of operations to generate equivalent expressions	Define, evaluate, and compare functions
Geometric measurement: understand concepts of volume and relate volume to multiplication and to addition	Reason about and solve one-variable equations and inequalities	Solve real-life and mathematical problems using numerical and algebraic expressions and equations	Use functions to model relationships between quantities
Graph points in the coordinate plane to solve real-world and mathematical problems*	Represent and analyze quantitative relationships between dependent and independent variables		

*Indicates a cluster that is well thought of as part of a student's progress to algebra, but that is currently not designated as Major by one or both of the assessment consortia in their draft materials. Apart from the asterisked exception, the clusters listed here are a subset of those designated as Major in both of the assessment consortia's draft documents.

Problem Types

Addition and Subtraction Problem Types

	Result Unknown
Add To	Three children are playing in the sandbox. Two more children come to play. How many children are playing in the sandbox now? *Situation and Solution Equation[1]:* $3 + 2 = \square$
Take From	Allyson has 10 dresses. She gives 4 to her friend. How many dresses does Allyson have now? *Situation and Solution Equation:* $10 - 4 = \square$

	Total Unknown	**Both Addends Unknown**
Put Together/ Take Apart	There are 5 red apples and 3 green apples in the fruit bowl. How many apples are in the fruit bowl? *Situation and Solution Equation:* $5 + 3 = \square$	Adam has 8 apples. How many can he put in the red fruit bowl and how many can he put in the green fruit bowl? *Situation Equation:* $8 = \square + \square$

[1]A situation equation represents the structure (action) in the problem situation. A solution equation shows the operation used to find the answer.

Teacher Notes

Critical Area

Common Core **CRITICAL AREA**

Representing, relating, and operating on whole numbers, initially with sets of objects

Personal Math Trainer

Look for this symbol for a gateway to your personalized learning path!

Number and Operations

	STUDENT RESOURCES	TEACHER RESOURCES

Domain Counting and Cardinality
Operations and Algebraic Thinking

■ K.CC.A   Know number names and the count sequence.

■ K.CC.B   Count to tell the number of objects.

■ K.OA.A   Understand addition as putting together and adding to, and understand subtraction as taking apart and taking from.

Common Core State Standards K.CC.A.3, K.CC.B.4a, K.CC.B.4b, K.CC.B.4c, K.OA.A.3

Domain Counting and Cardinality

■ K.CC.C   Compare numbers.

Common Core State Standards K.CC.C.6

© Houghton Mifflin Harcourt Publishing Company • Image Credits: (l) Photodisc/Getty Images

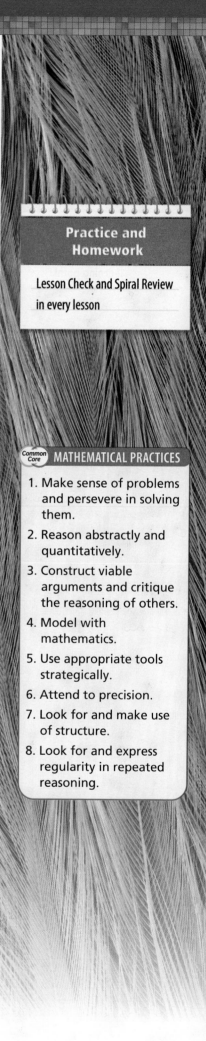

Practice and Homework

Lesson Check and Spiral Review in every lesson

Common Core MATHEMATICAL PRACTICES

1. Make sense of problems and persevere in solving them.
2. Reason abstractly and quantitatively.
3. Construct viable arguments and critique the reasoning of others.
4. Model with mathematics.
5. Use appropriate tools strategically.
6. Attend to precision.
7. Look for and make use of structure.
8. Look for and express regularity in repeated reasoning.

© Houghton Mifflin Harcourt Publishing Company • Image Credits: (r) Photodisc/Getty Images

Key: SE—Student Edition; **TE**—Teacher Edition

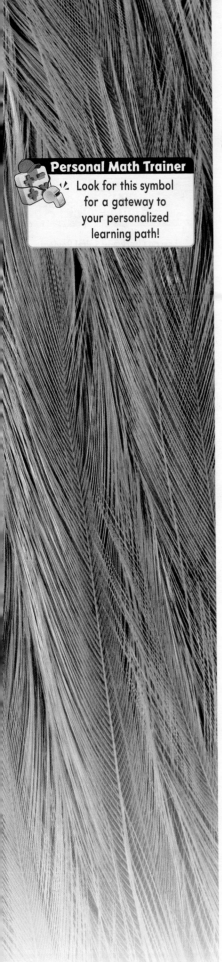

4 Represent and Compare Numbers to 10 . . . . SE—177 . . TE—177

Domain Counting and Cardinality
Operations and Algebraic Thinking

  K.CC.A   Know number names and the count sequence.

  K.CC.B   Count to tell the number of objects.

  K.CC.C   Compare numbers.

  K.OA.A   Understand addition as putting together and adding to, and understand subtraction as taking apart and taking from.

Common Core State Standards K.CC.A.2, K.CC.A.3, K.CC.B.5, K.CC.C.6, K.CC.C.7, K.OA.A.3, K.OA.A.4

Key: **SE**—Student Edition; **TE**—Teacher Edition

Practice and Homework

Lesson Check and Spiral Review in every lesson

Common Core MATHEMATICAL PRACTICES

1. Make sense of problems and persevere in solving them.
2. Reason abstractly and quantitatively.
3. Construct viable arguments and critique the reasoning of others.
4. Model with mathematics.
5. Use appropriate tools strategically.
6. Attend to precision.
7. Look for and make use of structure.
8. Look for and express regularity in repeated reasoning.

© Houghton Mifflin Harcourt Publishing Company • Image Credits: (r) Photodisc/Getty Images

Personal Math Trainer

Look for this symbol for a gateway to your personalized learning path!

Geometry and Positions

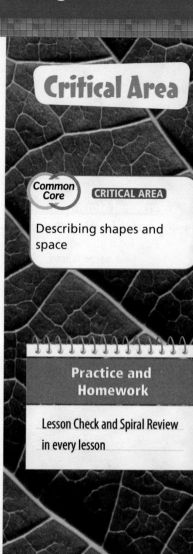
Critical Area

Domain Geometry

- ○ K.G.A   Identify and describe shapes.
- ☐ K.G.B   Analyze, compare, create, and compose shapes.

Common Core State Standards K.G.A.2, K.G.B.4, K.G.B.6

Common Core **CRITICAL AREA**

Describing shapes and space

Practice and Homework

Lesson Check and Spiral Review in every lesson

Common Core **MATHEMATICAL PRACTICES**

1. Make sense of problems and persevere in solving them.
2. Reason abstractly and quantitatively.
3. Construct viable arguments and critique the reasoning of others.
4. Model with mathematics.
5. Use appropriate tools strategically.
6. Attend to precision.
7. Look for and make use of structure.
8. Look for and express regularity in repeated reasoning.

© Houghton Mifflin Harcourt Publishing Company • Image Credits: (r) Photodisc/Getty Images

Key: SE—Student Edition; **TE**—Teacher Edition

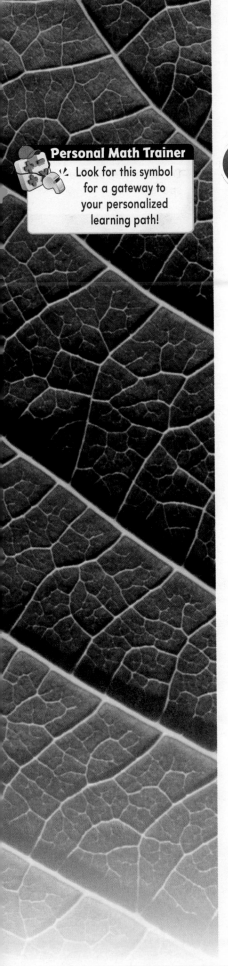

Personal Math Trainer
Look for this symbol for a gateway to your personalized learning path!

	STUDENT RESOURCES	TEACHER RESOURCES

10 Identify and Describe Three-Dimensional Shapes . . . . SE—569 . . TE—569

Domain Geometry

○ K.G.A   Identify and describe shapes.

☐ K.G.B   Analyze, compare, create, and compose shapes.

Common Core State Standards K.G.A.1, K.G.A.2, K.G.A.3, K.G.B.4, K.G.B.5

Measurement and Data

	STUDENT RESOURCES	TEACHER RESOURCES

Domains Measurement and Data

○ K.MD.A   Describe and compare measureable attributes.

Common Core State Standards K.MD.A.1, K.MD.A.2

	STUDENT RESOURCES	TEACHER RESOURCES

Domain Measurement and Data

☐ K.MD.B   Classify objects and count the number of objects in categories.

Common Core State Standards K.MD.B.3

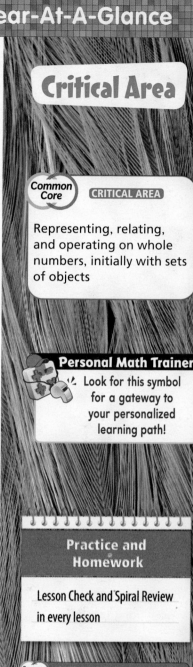

Critical Area

Common Core CRITICAL AREA

Representing, relating, and operating on whole numbers, initially with sets of objects

Personal Math Trainer

Look for this symbol for a gateway to your personalized learning path!

Practice and Homework

Lesson Check and Spiral Review in every lesson

Common Core MATHEMATICAL PRACTICES

1. Make sense of problems and persevere in solving them.

2. Reason abstractly and quantitatively.

3. Construct viable arguments and critique the reasoning of others.

4. Model with mathematics.

5. Use appropriate tools strategically.

6. Attend to precision.

7. Look for and make use of structure.

8. Look for and express regularity in repeated reasoning.

Key: SE—Student Edition; **TE**—Teacher Edition

End-of-Year Resources

Projects

Getting Ready for Grade 1

Key: **P**—Online Projects; **PG**—Planning Guide

Teacher Notes

Online Projects

Review Project:

Let's Plant a Garden

CRITICAL AREA Representing, relating, and operating on whole numbers, initially with sets of objects

Print Resources
• Planning Guide, p. PG42

Review Project:

Shape Search

CRITICAL AREA Describing shapes and space

Print Resources
• Planning Guide, p. PG44

Review Project:

Measurement Hunt

CRITICAL AREA Representing, relating, and operating on whole numbers, initially with sets of objects

Print Resources
• Planning Guide, p. PG46

 Common Core

Getting Ready Lessons build on Kindergarten content and prepare students for Grade 1 content.

Daily Pacing Chart

Review Projects	Lessons	Assessment	Total
3 days	20 days	2 days	25 days

LESSON 1 HANDS ON: **Add One**

COMMON CORE   K.OA.A.1, 1.OA.C.6

Resources
• Student Lesson Pages, Online
• Planning Guide, p. PG48

LESSON 5 HANDS ON: **Equal Sets**

COMMON CORE   K.OA.A.1, 1.OA.C.6

Resources
• Student Lesson Pages, Online
• Planning Guide, p. PG56

LESSON 6 **Related Addition Equations**

COMMON CORE   K.OA.A.1, 1.OA.C.6

Resources
• Student Lesson Pages, Online
• Planning Guide, p. PG58

LESSON 10 ALGEBRA: **Missing Part**

COMMON CORE   K.OA.A.1, 1.OA.C.6

Resources
• Student Lesson Pages, Online
• Planning Guide, p. PG66

LESSON 11 **Related Subtraction Equations**

COMMON CORE   K.OA.A.1, 1.OA.C.6

Resources
• Student Lesson Pages, Online
• Planning Guide, p. PG68

LESSON 15 **Read and Write Numbers 20 to 30**

COMMON CORE   K.CC.A.1, 1.NBT.A.1

Resources
• Student Lesson Pages, Online
• Planning Guide, p. PG78

LESSON 16 **Read and Write Numbers 30 to 40**

COMMON CORE   K.CC.A.1, 1.NBT.A.1

Resources
• Student Lesson Pages, Online
• Planning Guide, p. PG80

LESSON 20 **Use a Digital Clock**

COMMON CORE   K.CC.A.3, 1.MD.B.3

Resources
• Student Lesson Pages, Online
• Planning Guide, p. PG88

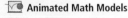

 Animated Math Models
✓ Assessment
MM HMH Mega Math
iT iTools
P Projects
ABC Multimedia eGlossary

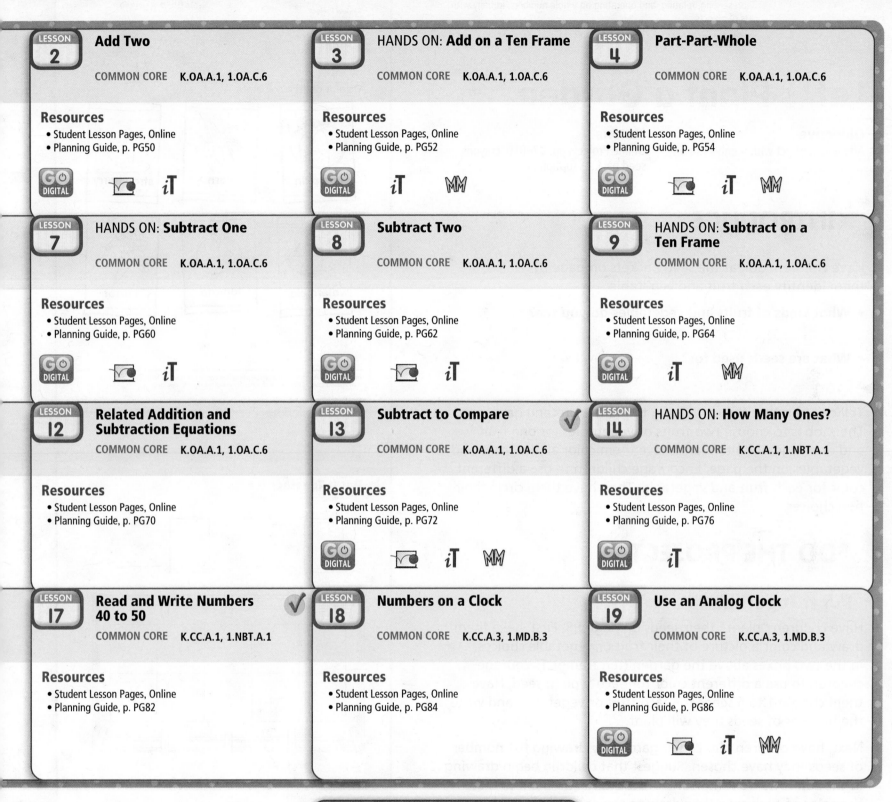

LESSON **2** Add Two

COMMON CORE K.OA.A.1, 1.OA.C.6

Resources
• Student Lesson Pages, Online
• Planning Guide, p. PG50

LESSON **3** HANDS ON: **Add on a Ten Frame**

COMMON CORE K.OA.A.1, 1.OA.C.6

Resources
• Student Lesson Pages, Online
• Planning Guide, p. PG52

LESSON **4** Part-Part-Whole

COMMON CORE K.OA.A.1, 1.OA.C.6

Resources
• Student Lesson Pages, Online
• Planning Guide, p. PG54

LESSON **7** HANDS ON: **Subtract One**

COMMON CORE K.OA.A.1, 1.OA.C.6

Resources
• Student Lesson Pages, Online
• Planning Guide, p. PG60

LESSON **8** Subtract Two

COMMON CORE K.OA.A.1, 1.OA.C.6

Resources
• Student Lesson Pages, Online
• Planning Guide, p. PG62

LESSON **9** HANDS ON: **Subtract on a Ten Frame**

COMMON CORE K.OA.A.1, 1.OA.C.6

Resources
• Student Lesson Pages, Online
• Planning Guide, p. PG64

LESSON **12** Related Addition and Subtraction Equations

COMMON CORE K.OA.A.1, 1.OA.C.6

Resources
• Student Lesson Pages, Online
• Planning Guide, p. PG70

LESSON **13** Subtract to Compare ✓

COMMON CORE K.OA.A.1, 1.OA.C.6

Resources
• Student Lesson Pages, Online
• Planning Guide, p. PG72

LESSON **14** HANDS ON: **How Many Ones?**

COMMON CORE K.CC.A.1, 1.NBT.A.1

Resources
• Student Lesson Pages, Online
• Planning Guide, p. PG76

LESSON **17** Read and Write Numbers 40 to 50 ✓

COMMON CORE K.CC.A.1, 1.NBT.A.1

Resources
• Student Lesson Pages, Online
• Planning Guide, p. PG82

LESSON **18** Numbers on a Clock

COMMON CORE K.CC.A.3, 1.MD.B.3

Resources
• Student Lesson Pages, Online
• Planning Guide, p. PG84

LESSON **19** Use an Analog Clock

COMMON CORE K.CC.A.3, 1.MD.B.3

Resources
• Student Lesson Pages, Online
• Planning Guide, p. PG86

✓ Assessment

An Assessment Check Mark following a lesson title indicates that a Checkpoint or Getting Ready Test is available for assessment after completing the lesson.

Checkpoints and Getting Ready Tests can be found in the online Getting Ready Lessons and Resources.

Representing, relating, and operating on whole numbers, initially with sets of objects

Let's Plant a Garden

Objective
Add and subtract with numbers to 5.

Materials
Online Projects pp. B7–B10, crayons, seed packets (optional)

1 INTRODUCE

Have children look at the seed packets on page B7. Help them identify each fruit and vegetable.

- **What kinds of fruits and vegetables do you see?** pumpkin, corn, strawberry, watermelon, tomato, carrot

- **What are seeds used for?** to grow fruits and vegetables

▶ Plan

Tell children that they are going to plant a pretend garden. Their job is to choose two fruits or vegetables (or one fruit and one vegetable) to plant. Have them color all the fruits and vegetables on the page. Encourage children to use a different color for each fruit and vegetable. Then have them circle their two choices.

2 DO THE PROJECT

▶ Put It Together

Have children "plant" their seeds on page B8. First, have them draw and color a picture of their fruit or vegetable choices in the two boxes above the garden (ten frame). Encourage children to use a different color for each type of seed. Have them choose 1 to 5 seeds for each fruit or vegetable, and write the number of seeds they will plant.

Next, have children plant their garden by drawing the number of seeds they have chosen. Suggest that children begin drawing in the top row, working from left to right. Ask them to match the color of each seed they draw to the color of the fruit or vegetable above. After they "plant" the first set of seeds, suggest they begin planting the second set in the next box of the ten frame. Have them record the total number of seeds.

- **How many of each seed did you plant?** Possible answer: 5 pumpkin seeds and 3 carrot seeds

- **How many seeds did you plant in all?** Possible answer: 8 seeds

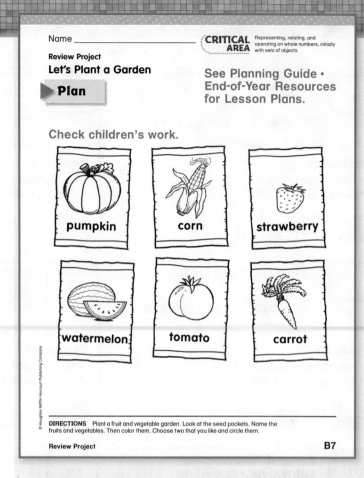

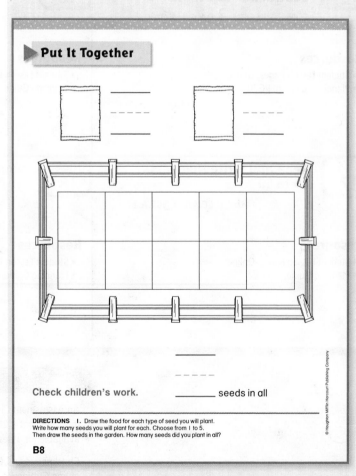

Name _____

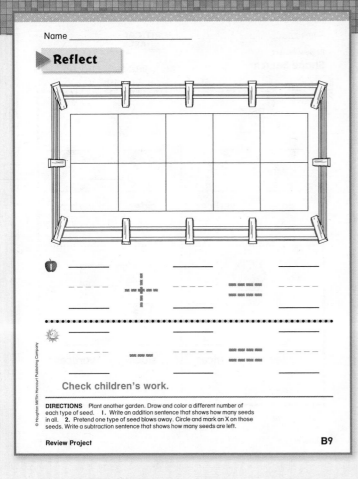

> **Reflect**

Check children's work.

DIRECTIONS Plant another garden. Draw and color a different number of each type of seed. 1. Write an addition sentence that shows how many seeds in all. 2. Pretend one type of seed blows away. Circle and mark an X on those seeds. Write a subtraction sentence that shows how many seeds are left.

Review Project   B9

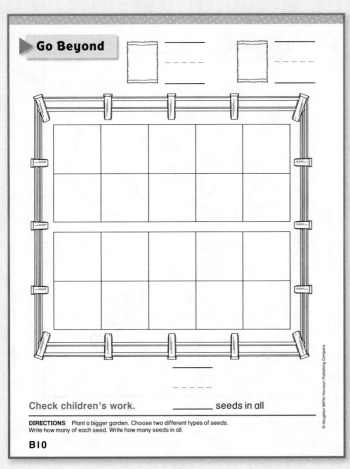

> **Go Beyond**

Check children's work. _____ seeds in all

DIRECTIONS Plant a bigger garden. Choose two different types of seeds. Write how many of each seed. Write how many seeds in all.

B10

▶ **Reflect**

Have children use the same types of seeds to plant another garden on page B9 using a different number of each type of seed. Suggest that they begin filling the garden (ten frame) in the top row, working from left to right.

- **How many seeds did you plant of each type?** Possible answer: 7 pumpkin seeds and 2 carrot seeds

- **How many seeds are left?** Possible answer: 7 seeds

▶ **Go Beyond**

Have them plant 6 to 10 of each seed to make a large garden. Suggest that they begin by filling the top ten frame.

- **What types of seeds did you plant this time? How many of each type did you plant?** Possible answers: corn and tomato; 8 corn seeds and 4 tomato seeds

- **How many seeds did you plant in all?** Possible answer: 12 seeds

③ EXTEND THE PROJECT

- Have children draw a picture of a garden on a sheet of paper and glue seeds onto the garden to show the seeds they will plant. Have children write the number of seeds.

- Have children compare the numbers of seeds and tell addition and subtraction word problems about them.

Portfolio You can use this project as a means of assessing a child's understanding of the concepts and skills found in this critical area.

Project Scoring Rubric

3 Demonstrates a full understanding of the project. Correctly represents each set of seeds and correctly records addition and subtraction sentences.

2 Demonstrates a thorough understanding of the project. May represent numbers or write a total with one or two errors.

1 Demonstrates a partial understanding of the project. May misrepresent numbers or write an incorrect total.

0 Demonstrates little understanding of the project. Fails to represent numbers correctly. Records incorrect totals and number sentences.

Shape Search

Objective
Identify, name, and describe two- and three-dimensional shapes, and demonstrate understanding of terms that describe positions of objects in the environment.

Materials
Online Projects pp. B11–B14, classroom objects, crayons, pattern blocks

1 INTRODUCE

Have children help you find examples of two-dimensional shapes in the classroom. Discuss the attributes that help identify each shape, such as the number of sides and vertices.

▶ Plan

Have children work with a partner. Tell children they will be searching for different types of shapes throughout this project. As you look at page B11 together, introduce the idea that they will be looking for these shapes in a scene on the next page. Help children count and record the number of sides and vertices for each shape.

- **How many sides does a triangle have?** 3 **Do all the sides of a triangle have to be the same length?** no

- **How are a square and rectangle alike? How are they different?** A square and rectangle each have 4 sides. The sides of a square have equal lengths. The rectangle has 2 short sides and 2 long sides.

2 DO THE PROJECT

▶ Put It Together

Have children identify some of the shapes they see on page B12. Help them color each shape according to the colors in the directions. You may want to make a key that helps children remember what color to use for each shape.

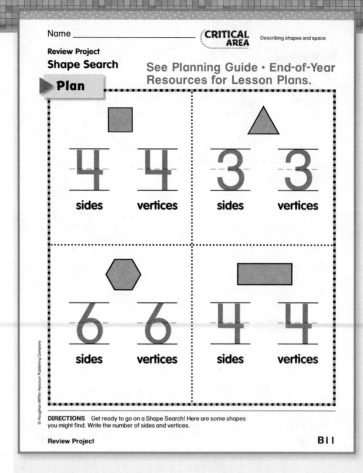

Name _____

Review Project
Shape Search

CRITICAL AREA   Describing shapes and space

See Planning Guide • End-of-Year Resources for Lesson Plans.

▶ **Plan**

| sides | vertices | sides | vertices |
| 4 | 4 | 3 | 3 |

| sides | vertices | sides | vertices |
| 6 | 6 | 4 | 4 |

DIRECTIONS Get ready to go on a Shape Search! Here are some shapes you might find. Write the number of sides and vertices.

Review Project   B11

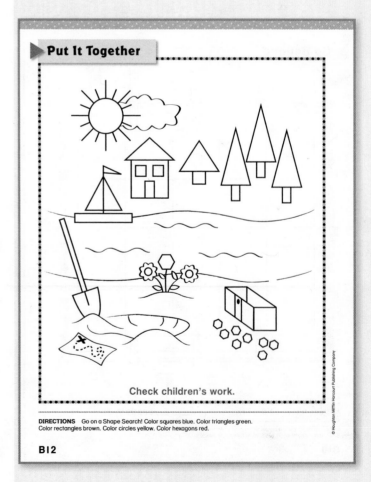

▶ **Put It Together**

Check children's work.

DIRECTIONS Go on a Shape Search! Color squares blue. Color triangles green. Color rectangles brown. Color circles yellow. Color hexagons red.

B12

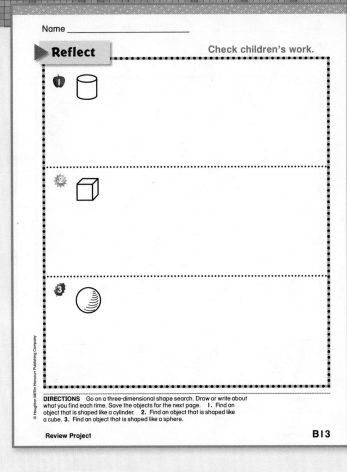

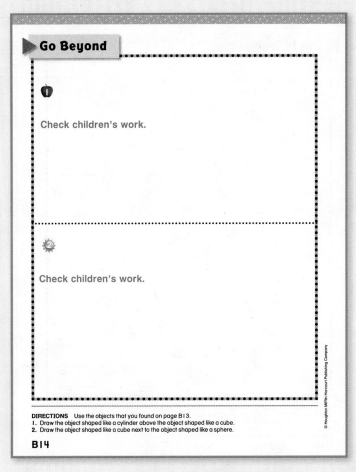

▶ Reflect

On page B13, encourage children to search for representations of the shapes pictured. Have children draw pictures of the examples they find.

▶ Go Beyond

On page B14, children draw pictures of the objects they found to demonstrate their understanding of the terms *above* and *next to*.

- **What object did you find that is shaped like a cylinder?** Possible answer: a pencil cup **What object did you find that is shaped like a cube?** Possible answer: a box of tissues

- **How can you show the box of tissues above the pencil holder?**

③ EXTEND THE PROJECT

- Have children use pattern blocks to make designs.
- **Place your blocks on a sheet of paper, and then trace your design.**
- Have children count the number of each type of shape they used.
- Ask questions to compare the number of shapes in their designs.

Project Scoring Rubric

3 Demonstrates a full understanding of the project. Correctly identifies and describes attributes of two- and three-dimensional shapes, and correctly uses terms to describe positions of objects in the environment.

2 Demonstrates a thorough understanding of the project. Correctly identifies most shapes and most attributes of two- and three-dimensional shapes, and correctly uses some terms to describe positions of objects in the environment.

1 Demonstrates a partial understanding of the project. Correctly identifies some shapes and some attributes of two- and three-dimensional shapes, and correctly uses the terms to describe positions of objects in the environment with errors.

0 Demonstrates little understanding of the project. Cannot distinguish shapes, identify attributes, or describe positions of objects in the environment.

Representing, relating, and operating on whole numbers, initially with sets of objects

Measurement Hunt

Objective
Measure length using connecting cubes, and compare objects by length and weight.

Materials
Online Review Projects pp. B15–B18, connecting cubes, classroom objects, crayons

1 INTRODUCE

Show children various classroom objects and discuss the different ways that objects can be described. Encourage them to think about measurable attributes by asking the following questions as you hold up two objects:

- **Which object is longer?** Answers will vary.

- **Which object is heavier?** Answers will vary.

▶ Plan

Tell children that they are going on a measurement hunt. They will compare objects to their shoe to determine which is longer and which is heavier. Have children trace their shoe on page B15. Guide children to mark a beginning and end point for the length. Then have them build a cube train that is about the same length as their shoe. Have them write how many cubes long the cube train is.

2 DO THE PROJECT

▶ Put It Together

On page B16, children hunt for objects in the classroom that are shorter than and longer than their shoe. They can use their shoe or the cube train they made as a measurement tool. After children find each object, have them build a cube train that is about the same length as the object. They should write how many cubes long the cube train is. Encourage children to compare the cube trains they build for each object and to discuss their results.

- **What object did you find that is longer than your shoe?** Possible answer: a book **About how many cubes long is the object you found?** Possible answer: about 12 cubes

- **What object did you find that is shorter than your shoe?** Possible answer: a crayon **About how many cubes long is the object you found?** Possible answer: about 5 cubes

- **Now compare the cube trains you made for each object. Which cube train is longer?** the cube train I made for the book

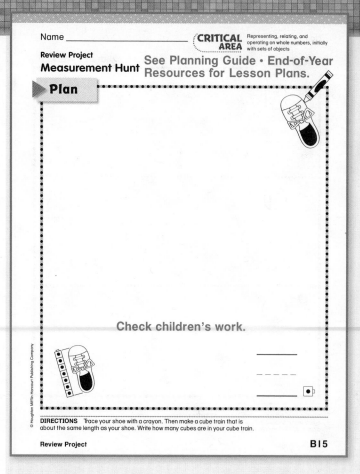

Name _____

CRITICAL AREA Representing, relating, and operating on whole numbers, initially with sets of objects

Review Project
Measurement Hunt

See Planning Guide • End-of-Year Resources for Lesson Plans.

▶ **Plan**

Check children's work.

DIRECTIONS Trace your shoe with a crayon. Then make a cube train that is about the same length as your shoe. Write how many cubes are in your cube train.

Review Project   B15

▶ **Put It Together**   Check children's work.

①

❋

DIRECTIONS Compare objects to the length of your shoe. Draw what you find each time. 1. Find an object that is shorter than your shoe. Make a cube train that is about the same length as the object you found. Write how many cubes are in your cube train. 2. Find an object that is longer than your shoe. Make a cube train that is about the same length as the object you found. Write how many cubes are in your cube train.

B16

Online Projects, pp. B15–B16

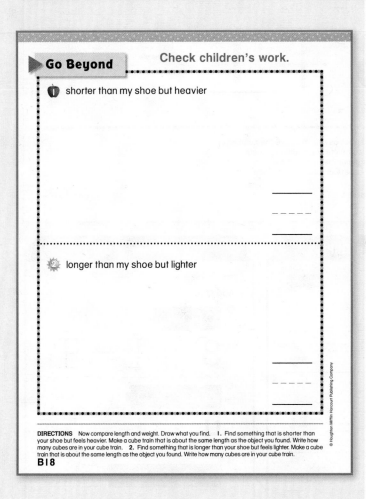

Name _____

▶ Reflect

Check children's work.

about as heavy as my shoe

heavier than my shoe

lighter than my shoe

DIRECTIONS Compare objects to the weight of your shoe. Find an object that is about the same weight, one that is heavier, and one that is lighter. Draw what you find each time.

Review Project

B17

▶ Go Beyond

Check children's work.

1 shorter than my shoe but heavier

_____
- - - - - -
_____

☀ longer than my shoe but lighter

_____
- - - - - -
_____

DIRECTIONS Now compare length and weight. Draw what you find. **1.** Find something that is shorter than your shoe but feels heavier. Make a cube train that is about the same length as the object you found. Write how many cubes are in your cube train. **2.** Find something that is longer than your shoe but feels lighter. Make a cube train that is about the same length as the object you found. Write how many cubes are in your cube train.

B18

▶ Reflect

On page B17, children compare the weight of classroom objects to the weight of their shoe. Suggest that children hold their shoe in one hand and the object in the other to compare the weights. Have children draw the objects and discuss their results.

▶ Go Beyond

On page B18, children explore the fact that size and weight are different attributes and may not be related. After children find each object, have them build a cube train that is about the same length as the object. They should write how many cubes long the cube train is.

③ EXTEND THE PROJECT

Have children trace their shoes, write their name on the tracing, and cut it out. Include a tracing of your own shoe, too. Have children help you order the pictures by length and discuss the results.

- **Whose shoe is longer, my shoe or Sam's shoe?** your shoe

- **Where would an adult's shoe go in the display?** right before or after the teacher's shoe

Project Scoring Rubric

Performance Assessment

3 Demonstrates a full understanding of the project. Understands how to compare objects by length or weight. Correctly uses vocabulary for comparisons.

2 Demonstrates a thorough understanding of the project. Understands that length and weight may be independent attributes while making an error or two. May make an error when comparing objects by length or weight, or when using vocabulary for comparisons.

1 Demonstrates a partial understanding of the project. Does not understand that length and weight may be independent attributes. May make errors when comparing objects by length or weight, or when using vocabulary for comparisons.

0 Demonstrates little understanding of the project. Does not know how to compare objects by length or weight. Uses incorrect vocabulary for comparisons.

LESSON 1

Hands On •
Add One

LESSON AT A GLANCE

Common Core Standards

Understand addition as putting together and adding to, and understand subtraction as taking apart and taking from.

K.OA.A.1 Represent addition and subtraction with objects, fingers, mental images, drawings, sounds (e.g., claps), acting out situations, verbal explanations, expressions, or equations.

Add and subtract within 20.

1.OA.C.6 Add and subtract within 20, demonstrating fluency for addition and subtraction within 10. Use strategies such as counting on; making ten (e.g., $8 + 6 = 8 + 2 + 4 = 10 + 4 = 14$); decomposing a number leading to a ten (e.g., $13 - 4 = 13 - 3 - 1 = 10 - 1 = 9$);

using the relationship between addition and subtraction (e.g., knowing that $8 + 4 = 12$, one knows $12 - 8 = 4$); and creating equivalent but easier or known sums (e.g., adding $6 + 7$ by creating the known equivalent $6 + 6 + 1 = 12 + 1 = 13$).

Lesson Objective
Use objects to add one and find the sum.

Essential Question
How can you use objects to add one?

Materials
MathBoard, connecting cubes

 GO DIGITAL

*i*T *i*Tools: Counters

Animated Math Models

1 TEACH and TALK **GO DIGITAL** • Animated Math Models

Materials connecting cubes

Display one cube.

- **How many cubes are there?** 1 **How can you add one more?** Add one more cube to it.

- **Using objects can help you see how many in all. Add one more cube. How many cubes in all?** 2

Write this as an addition sentence.

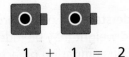

$$1 + 1 = 2$$

Write the addition sentence and read it together.

This lesson builds on the concept of addition presented in Chapter 5 and prepares children for the concept of counting on taught in Grade 1.

Name _____

Lesson 1

Add One

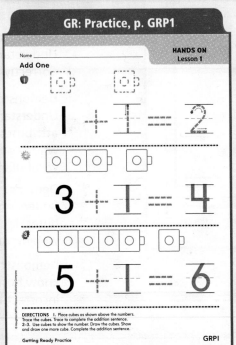

DIRECTIONS 1. Place cubes as shown above the numbers. Trace the cubes. Trace to complete the addition sentence. 2–3. Use cubes to show the number. Draw the cubes. Show and draw one more cube. Complete the addition sentence.

Getting Ready for Grade 1

one **GR1**

© Houghton Mifflin Harcourt Publishing Company

GR: Practice, p. GRP1

Name _____

HANDS ON Lesson 1

Add One

DIRECTIONS 1. Place cubes as shown above the numbers. Trace the cubes. Trace to complete the addition sentence. 2–3. Use cubes to show the number. Draw the cubes. Show and draw one more cube. Complete the addition sentence.

Getting Ready Practice

GRP1

GR: Reteach, p. GRR1

Name _____

Lesson 1 Reteach

Add One

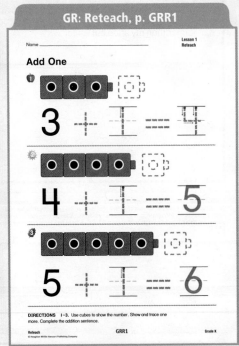

DIRECTIONS 1–3. Use cubes to show the number. Show and trace one more. Complete the addition sentence.

Reteach

GRR1

Grade K

---

*GR – Getting Ready Lessons and Resources (*www.thinkcentral.com*)

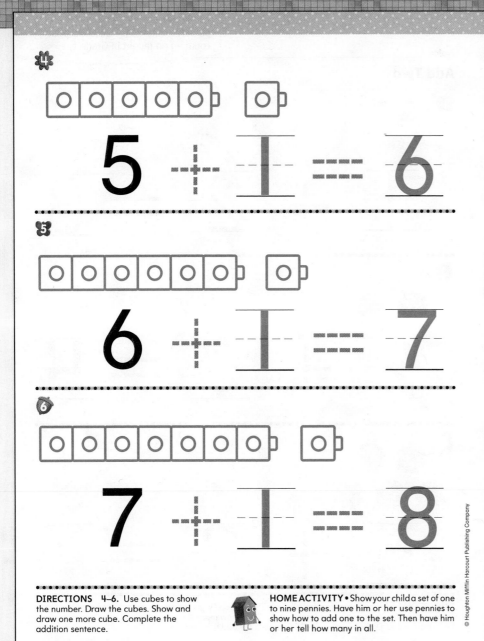

4

$$5 + 1 = 6$$

5

$$6 + 1 = 7$$

6

$$7 + 1 = 8$$

DIRECTIONS 4–6. Use cubes to show the number. Draw the cubes. Show and draw one more cube. Complete the addition sentence.

GR2 two

HOME ACTIVITY • Show your child a set of one to nine pennies. Have him or her use pennies to show how to add one to the set. Then have him or her tell how many in all.

- **Explain how using objects helps you add one more.** Possible answer: By adding one more object, I can count on one more to find how many in all.

Some children will be able to add one without recounting the initial group. This will prepare children for the strategy *count on* in Grade 1.

2 PRACTICE

Materials connecting cubes

Explain that in this lesson children first model the number with cubes. They draw the cubes, add one cube, and draw that cube. They will then complete the addition sentence to show what they modeled.

- **In Exercise 1 trace the cube above the number 1. Now trace the other cube and the number 1. What is 1 + 1 equal to?** 2 **Trace the number 2.** Read the completed addition sentence together.

Have children locate Exercise 2.

- **Use cubes to show the number. Draw the cubes. Show and draw one more cube. What is 2 + 1 equal to?** 3 **Write the number 3.**

Read the completed addition sentence together. Repeat the process for the remaining exercises. Remind children to trace the *plus* and *is equal to* symbols. Read the completed addition sentences together.

3 SUMMARIZE

 **MATHEMATICAL PRACTICES**

Essential Question

How can you use objects to add one? I show one more cube. I can count on one more to find how many in all.

Math Journal  Math

Draw 2 cubes. Draw to show 1 more cube. Write how many in all.

Add Two

LESSON AT A GLANCE

Common Core Standards
Understand addition as putting together and adding to, and understand subtraction as taking apart and taking from.
K.OA.A.1 Represent addition and subtraction with objects, fingers, mental images, drawings, sounds (e.g., claps), acting out situations, verbal explanations, expressions, or equations.

Add and subtract within 20.
1.OA.C.6 Add and subtract within 20, demonstrating fluency for addition and subtraction within 10. Use strategies such as counting on; making ten (e.g., $8 + 6 = 8 + 2 + 4 = 10 + 4 = 14$); decomposing a number leading to a ten (e.g., $13 - 4 = 13 - 3 - 1 = 10 - 1 = 9$);

using the relationship between addition and subtraction (e.g., knowing that $8 + 4 = 12$, one knows $12 - 8 = 4$); and creating equivalent but easier or known sums (e.g., adding $6 + 7$ by creating the known equivalent $6 + 6 + 1 = 12 + 1 = 13$).

Lesson Objective
Use pictures to add two and find the sum.

Essential Question
How can you add two?

Materials
MathBoard

Animated Math Models
*i*Tools: Counters

1 TEACH and TALK
GO DIGITAL • Animated Math Models

Draw a set of three objects and a set of two objects on the board.

• **How many objects are in the first set?** 3

Write the number **3** on the board followed by a *plus* symbol.

• **How many objects are in the next set?** 2

Write the number **2** and the *is equal to* symbol.

• **How many objects are there in all?** 5

Write the number **5** to complete the addition sentence.

Some children may recognize how many are in the first set without counting. They may also be able to use mental math to find how many in all.

This lesson builds on the concept of addition presented in Chapter 5 and prepares children for the concept of counting on taught in Grade 1.

Name _____

Add Two

1

$$1 + 2 = 3$$

2

$$2 + 2 = 4$$

3

$$5 + 2 = 7$$

© Houghton Mifflin Harcourt Publishing Company

DIRECTIONS 1. Count how many shells in the first group. Trace the two shells. Trace to complete the addition sentence. 2–3. Count how many shells. Write the number. Draw two more shells. Complete the addition sentence.

Getting Ready for Grade 1 three **GR3**

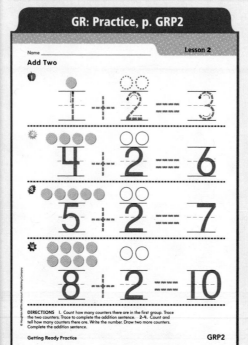

GR: Practice, p. GRP2

Name _____ Lesson **2**
Add Two

1 $$1 + 2 = 3$$

2 $$4 + 2 = 6$$

3 $$5 + 2 = 7$$

4 $$8 + 2 = 10$$

DIRECTIONS 1. Count how many counters there are in the first group. Trace the two counters. Trace to complete the addition sentence. 2–4. Count and tell how many counters there are. Write the number. Draw two more counters. Complete the addition sentence.

Getting Ready Practice GRP2

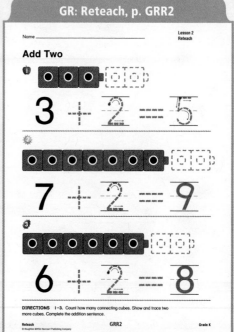

GR: Reteach, p. GRR2

Name _____ Lesson 2
Reteach
Add Two

1 $$3 + 2 = 5$$

2 $$7 + 2 = 9$$

3 $$6 + 2 = 8$$

DIRECTIONS 1–3. Count how many connecting cubes. Show and trace two more cubes. Complete the addition sentence.

Reteach GRR2 Grade K

*GR – Getting Ready Lessons and Resources (*www.thinkcentral.com*)

$4 + 2 = 6$

$8 + 2 = 10$

$3 + 2 = 5$

DIRECTIONS 4–6. Count how many shells there are. Write the number. Draw two more shells. Complete the addition sentence.

HOME ACTIVITY • Draw objects in a column beginning with a set of 1 to a set of 8. Have your child draw two more objects beside each set, and write how many in all.

© Houghton Mifflin Harcourt Publishing Company

GR4 four

---

2 PRACTICE

Have children locate Exercise 1.
- **How many shells are in the first set?** 1
- **Trace the shells in the next set. How many did you trace?** 2
- **Trace the addition sentence. How many shells in all?** 3

Have children locate Exercise 2.
- **How many shells do you see?** 2
- **How many more shells are you going to draw?** 2
- **Write the addition sentence. Write how many in all.** 4

Repeat with similar questions for the remaining exercises. Read the completed addition sentences together.

3 SUMMARIZE

Common Core **MATHEMATICAL PRACTICES**

Essential Question

How can you add two? I can look at the pictures to see how many and know that I need to add two more to find how many in all.

Math Journal Math

Draw 3 circles. Draw 2 more circles. Write how many in all.

LESSON 3

Hands On • Add on a Ten Frame

LESSON AT A GLANCE

Common Core Standards

Understand addition as putting together and adding to, and understand subtraction as taking apart and taking from.

K.OA.A.1 Represent addition and subtraction with objects, fingers, mental images, drawings, sounds (e.g., claps), acting out situations, verbal explanations, expressions, or equations.

Add and subtract within 20.

1.OA.C.6 Add and subtract within 20, demonstrating fluency for addition and subtraction within 10. Use strategies such as counting on; making ten (e.g., $8 + 6 = 8 + 2 + 4 = 10 + 4 = 14$); decomposing a number leading to a ten (e.g., $13 - 4 = 13 - 3 - 1 = 10 - 1 = 9$);

using the relationship between addition and subtraction (e.g., knowing that $8 + 4 = 12$, one knows $12 - 8 = 4$); and creating equivalent but easier or known sums (e.g., adding $6 + 7$ by creating the known equivalent $6 + 6 + 1 = 12 + 1 = 13$).

Lesson Objective
Add facts to 10 on a ten frame.

Essential Question
How can you use a ten frame to add?

Materials
MathBoard, two-color counters

*i*Tools: Counters
HMH Mega Math

1 TEACH and TALK
Animated Math Models

Materials Workmat 3 (ten frames) (see *eTeacher Resources*), two-color counters

Have children place six red counters in the ten frame. Now have them place four yellow counters to fill the ten frame. Make sure they start at the top left of the ten frame and fill that row first.

- **How many red counters are there?** 6
- **How many yellow counters are there?** 4
- **What addition sentence can you write to show how many counters in all?** $6 + 4 = 10$

This lesson builds on the concept of addition presented in Chapter 5 and prepares children for addition skills and strategies taught in Grade 1.

Name _____

Add on a Ten Frame

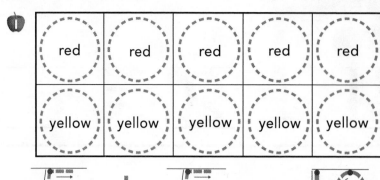

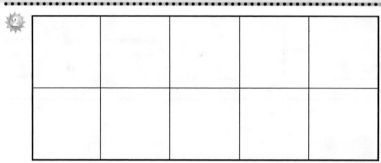

Check children's work.

DIRECTIONS 1. Place counters on the ten frame as shown. Trace the addition sentence. 2. Place some counters red side up on the ten frame. Add more counters yellow side up to fill the ten frame. Complete the addition sentence.

Getting Ready for Grade 1   five **GR5**

GR: Practice, p. GRP3

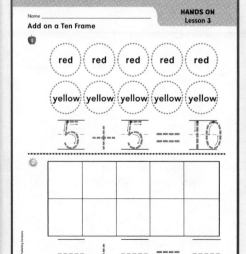

GR: Reteach, p. GRR3

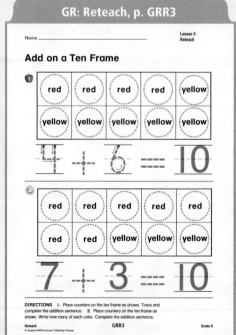

*GR – Getting Ready Lessons and Resources (www.thinkcentral.com)

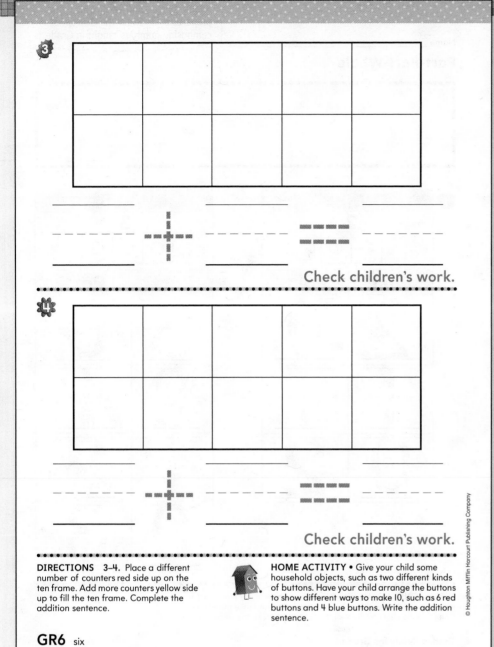

Check children's work.

Check children's work.

DIRECTIONS 3–4. Place a different number of counters red side up on the ten frame. Add more counters yellow side up to fill the ten frame. Complete the addition sentence.

HOME ACTIVITY • Give your child some household objects, such as two different kinds of buttons. Have your child arrange the buttons to show different ways to make 10, such as 6 red buttons and 4 blue buttons. Write the addition sentence.

GR6 six

© Houghton Mifflin Harcourt Publishing Company

---

 2 PRACTICE MATH BOARD

Materials two-color counters

Have children look at Exercise 1.

- **How many red counters will you place in the ten frame?** 5
- **How many yellow counters will you place in the ten frame?** 5

Trace the addition sentence to show how many counters in all.

Have children complete Exercises 2–4 using different sets of red and yellow counters to fill the ten frame. Then have them complete the addition sentence to match the counters. Discuss the different addition facts for ten that children modeled on the ten frame.

3 SUMMARIZE

Common Core MATHEMATICAL PRACTICES

Essential Question

How can you use a ten frame to add? I can place two colors of counters to fill the ten frame and know that the two groups of counters show 10.

Math Journal  WRITE Math

Draw a row of 5 red counters and a row of 5 yellow counters. Write how many counters in all.

LESSON 4

Part-Part-Whole

LESSON AT A GLANCE

Common Core Standards

Understand addition as putting together and adding to, and understand subtraction as taking apart and taking from.

K.OA.A.1 Represent addition and subtraction with objects, fingers, mental images, drawings, sounds (e.g., claps), acting out situations, verbal explanations, expressions, or equations.

Add and subtract within 20.

1.OA.C.6 Add and subtract within 20, demonstrating fluency for addition and subtraction within 10. Use strategies such as counting on; making ten (e.g., $8 + 6 = 8 + 2 + 4 = 10 + 4 = 14$); decomposing a number leading to a ten (e.g., $13 - 4 = 13 - 3 - 1 = 10 - 1 = 9$);

using the relationship between addition and subtraction (e.g., knowing that $8 + 4 = 12$, one knows $12 - 8 = 4$); and creating equivalent but easier or known sums (e.g., adding $6 + 7$ by creating the known equivalent $6 + 6 + 1 = 12 + 1 = 13$).

Lesson Objective
Find the parts that make the whole.

Essential Question
How can you find the parts that make the whole?

Materials
MathBoard, connecting cubes

  Animated Math Models

iT iTools: Counters

MM HMH Mega Math

1 TEACH and TALK

GO DIGITAL * Animated Math Models

Materials connecting cubes

Show children a six-cube train.

• **How many cubes are there?** 6

Break the cube train so you have a four-cube train and a two-cube train. Show children the two parts that make the whole.

• **How many cubes are in this cube train?** 4

• **How many cubes are in this cube train?** 2

• **What can you tell me about the two parts of 6?** 6 is made up of two parts of 4 and 2.

This lesson builds on the concept of addition presented in Chapter 5 and prepares children for the concept of composing numbers taught in Grade 1.

Name _____

Part-Part-Whole

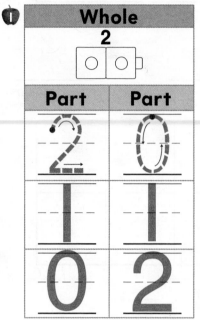

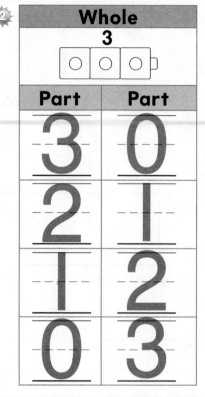

© Houghton Mifflin Harcourt Publishing Company

DIRECTIONS 1–2. How many cubes are there in all? Place that many cubes in the workspace. Show the parts that make the whole. Complete the chart to show all the parts that make the whole.

Getting Ready for Grade 1 seven **GR7**

GR: Practice, p. GRP4

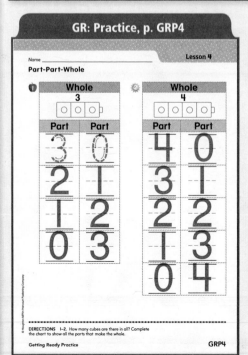

GR: Reteach, p. GRR4

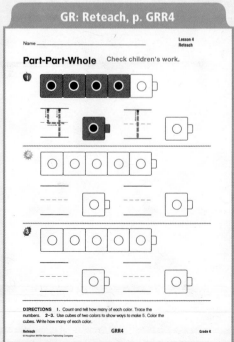

*GR – Getting Ready Lessons and Resources (www.thinkcentral.com)

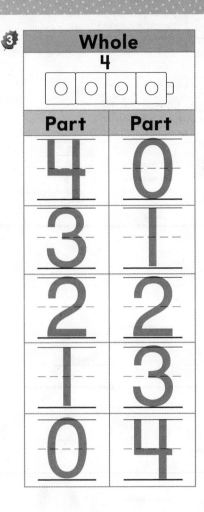

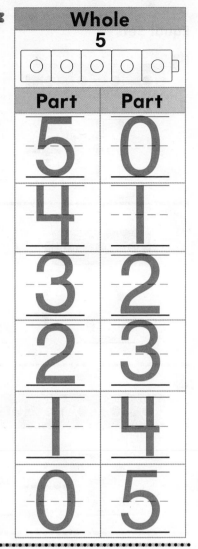

3

Whole 4	
Part	Part
4	0
3	1
2	2
1	3
0	4

4

Whole 5	
Part	Part
5	0
4	1
3	2
2	3
1	4
0	5

© Houghton Mifflin Harcourt Publishing Company

DIRECTIONS 3–4. How many cubes are there in all? Complete the chart to show all the parts that make the whole.

 HOME ACTIVITY • Have your child use buttons or macaroni pieces to show the different parts that make the whole set of 8 (e.g. 7 and 1, 6 and 2, 5 and 3, 4 and 4.)

GR8 eight

2 PRACTICE

Materials connecting cubes

Have children look at Exercise 1. They may need to use the workspace at the top of the page to model the parts that make the whole.

• **How many cubes are there in all?** 2

• **If you have 2 cubes in one part of 2, how many cubes would be in the other part?** 0

Trace the numbers to show the parts.

• **If 1 is one part of 2, what would the other part be?** 1

Write those numbers on your chart. Continue to write the other parts that make 2.

Have children complete Exercise 2 using all the different parts that make 3.

Have children complete Exercises 3 and 4 in a similar way. Discuss all the different parts that make 4 and 5.

3 SUMMARIZE

 **MATHEMATICAL PRACTICES**

Essential Question

How can you find the parts that make the whole? I can look at the whole and break it apart to find two parts that make the whole.

Math Journal WRITE Math

Draw cube trains to show all the parts that make the whole set of 3.

LESSON 5

Hands On • Equal Sets

LESSON AT A GLANCE

Common Core Standards
Understand addition as putting together and adding to, and understand subtraction as taking apart and taking from.
K.OA.A.1 Represent addition and subtraction with objects, fingers, mental images, drawings, sounds (e.g., claps), acting out situations, verbal explanations, expressions, or equations.

Add and subtract within 20.
1.OA.C.6 Add and subtract within 20, demonstrating fluency for addition and subtraction within 10. Use strategies such as counting on; making ten (e.g., $8 + 6 = 8 + 2 + 4 = 10 + 4 = 14$); decomposing a number leading to a ten (e.g., $13 - 4 = 13 - 3 - 1 = 10 - 1 = 9$);

using the relationship between addition and subtraction (e.g., knowing that $8 + 4 = 12$, one knows $12 - 8 = 4$); and creating equivalent but easier or known sums (e.g., adding $6 + 7$ by creating the known equivalent $6 + 6 + 1 = 12 + 1 = 13$).

Lesson Objective
Model and write doubles facts.

Essential Question
How can you add two equal amounts?

Materials
MathBoard, connecting cubes

GO DIGITAL
▭ Animated Math Models
iT iTools: Counters

1 TEACH and TALK
GO DIGITAL ° Animated Math Models

Materials connecting cubes

Show children two 2-cube trains, one red and one blue. Hold one above the other so that children can see that the number of cubes matches.

- **How many cubes are in this red cube train?** 2

- **How many cubes are in this blue cube train?** 2

- **Do the numbers match?** yes

Join the 2-cube trains to make a 4-cube train.

- **How many cubes are there in all?** 4

- **What addition sentence can you write to show how many 2 and 2 are?** $2 + 2 = 4$

This lesson builds on basic addition concepts presented in Chapter 5 and prepares children for addition within 20 taught in Grade 1.

Name _____

Equal Sets

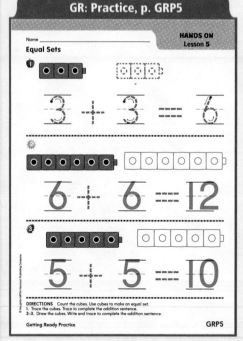

DIRECTIONS Count the cubes. Use cubes to make an equal set. 1. Trace the cubes. Trace the addition sentence. 2–3. Draw the cubes. Write and trace to complete the addition sentence.

Getting Ready for Grade 1   nine **GR9**

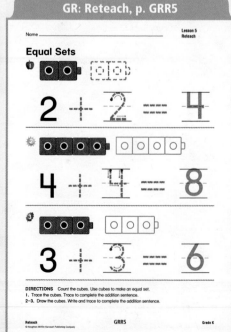

*GR – Getting Ready Lessons and Resources (*www.thinkcentral.com*)

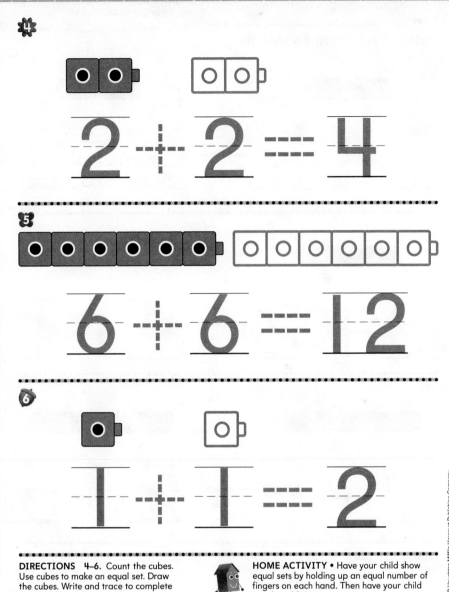

DIRECTIONS 4–6. Count the cubes. Use cubes to make an equal set. Draw the cubes. Write and trace to complete the addition sentence.

HOME ACTIVITY • Have your child show equal sets by holding up an equal number of fingers on each hand. Then have your child say the addition sentence.

© Houghton Mifflin Harcourt Publishing Company

GR10 ten

2 PRACTICE

Materials connecting cubes

Have children look at Exercise 1.

- **How many cubes are in the cube train?** 4
- **How do you make a cube train that matches?** You use 4 cubes.

Instruct children to make a 4-cube train and then trace the cubes.

- **What is the sum of 4 and 4?** 8
- **What is the addition sentence?** 4 + 4 = 8

Have children trace the addition sentence.

Have children locate Exercise 2.

- **How many cubes are in the cube train?** 3
- **How many cubes will your matching cube train have?** 3 cubes **Where will you draw your cube train?** next to the 3 that are already there
- **What addition sentence will you write?** 3 + 3 = 6

Continue with similar questions for Exercises 3–6. Then read the completed doubles facts together as a class.

3 SUMMARIZE

Common Core **MATHEMATICAL PRACTICES**

Essential Question

How can you add two equal amounts? I can make 2 matching cube trains and write the addition sentence.

Math Journal  Math

Draw a cube train with 3 cubes. Then use cubes to make an equal set. Draw the cubes.

Getting Ready Lessons and Resources, pp. GR11–GR12 ✓ **Checkpoint**

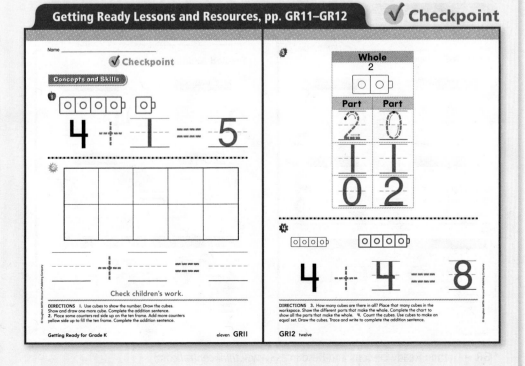

Related Addition Equations

LESSON AT A GLANCE

Common Core Standards
Understand addition as putting together and adding to, and understand subtraction as taking apart and taking from.
K.OA.A.1 Represent addition and subtraction with objects, fingers, mental images, drawings, sounds (e.g., claps), acting out situations, verbal explanations, expressions, or equations.

Add and subtract within 20.
1.OA.C.6 Add and subtract within 20, demonstrating fluency for addition and subtraction within 10. Use strategies such as counting on; making ten (e.g., $8 + 6 = 8 + 2 + 4 = 10 + 4 = 14$); decomposing a number leading to a ten (e.g., $13 - 4 = 13 - 3 - 1 = 10 - 1 = 9$);

using the relationship between addition and subtraction (e.g., knowing that $8 + 4 = 12$, one knows $12 - 8 = 4$); and creating equivalent but easier or known sums (e.g., adding $6 + 7$ by creating the known equivalent $6 + 6 + 1 = 12 + 1 = 13$).

Lesson Objective
Identify equivalent addition expressions.

Essential Question
How do you know if two different addition facts are equal?

Materials
MathBoard

 GO DIGITAL

iT *i*Tools: Counters

1 TEACH and TALK **GO DIGITAL** • Animated Math Models

Materials connecting cubes

Show children a cube train with 4 red cubes and 4 blue cubes.

- **I used 8 cubes. How many cubes are red?** 4 **How many cubes are blue?** 4

Write **4 + 4** on the board. Then show children a cube train with 1 red cube and 7 blue cubes.

- **I made 8 in a different way. How many cubes are red?** 1 **How many cubes are blue?** 7

Write **1 + 7** on the board. Then hold up both cube trains.

- **Is 4 + 4 equal to 1 + 7?** Yes, they are both 8.

On the board, add an *is equal to* symbol to show that $4 + 4 = 1 + 7$. Read the equation.

PG58 **Planning Guide**

> This lesson builds on basic addition concepts presented in Chapter 5 and prepares children for addition within 20 taught in Grade 1.

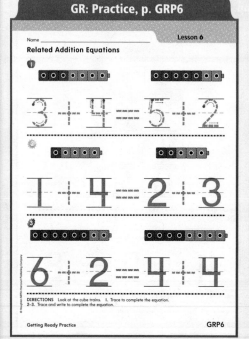

DIRECTIONS Look at the cube trains. **1.** Trace to complete the equation. **2–3.** Trace and write to complete the equation.

Getting Ready for Grade 1   *thirteen* **GR13**

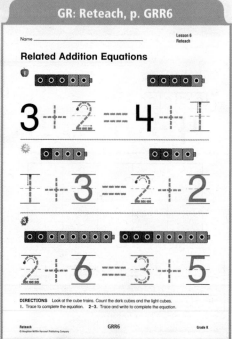

GR: Practice, p. GRP6

GR: Reteach, p. GRR6

*GR – Getting Ready Lessons and Resources (*www.thinkcentral.com*)

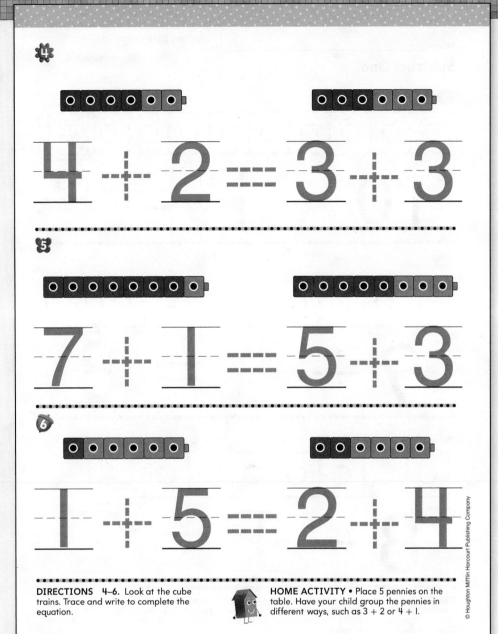

4

4 + 2 = 3 + 3

5

7 + 1 = 5 + 3

6

1 + 5 = 2 + 4

DIRECTIONS 4–6. Look at the cube trains. Trace and write to complete the equation.

HOME ACTIVITY • Place 5 pennies on the table. Have your child group the pennies in different ways, such as 3 + 2 or 4 + 1.

© Houghton Mifflin Harcourt Publishing Company

GR14 fourteen

© Houghton Mifflin Harcourt Publishing Company

2 PRACTICE

Materials connecting cubes

Have children look at Exercise 1.

- **How many cubes are in each of the cube trains?** 4
- **In the first cube train, what numbers make 4?** 1 and 3 **In the second cube train, what numbers make 4?** 2 and 2
- **What equation shows these two different ways to make 4?** 1 + 3 = 2 + 2

Have children trace the equation.

Have children locate Exercise 2.

- **How many cubes are in each of the cube trains?** 5
- **In the first cube train, what numbers make 5?** 3 and 2 **What will you write below the cube train?** 3 + 2
- **In the second cube train, what numbers make 5?** 4 and 1 **What will you write below the cube train?** 4 + 1
- **Is 3 + 2 equal to 4 + 1?** yes

Have children trace the *is equal to* symbol.

Continue with similar questions for Exercises 3–6. Then read the completed equations together as a class.

3 SUMMARIZE

Common Core **MATHEMATICAL PRACTICES**

Essential Question

How do you know if two different addition facts are equal? I can look at cube trains that show the addition facts. If the cube trains have the same number of cubes, the facts are equal.

Math Journal Math

Show a cube train with 5 red cubes and 1 blue cube. Show another cube train with 3 red cubes and 3 blue cubes. Draw the cube trains. Tell the equation.

LESSON 7

Hands On • Subtract One

LESSON AT A GLANCE

Common Core Standards

Understand addition as putting together and adding to, and understand subtraction as taking apart and taking from.

K.OA.A.1 Represent addition and subtraction with objects, fingers, mental images, drawings, sounds (e.g., claps), acting out situations, verbal explanations, expressions, or equations.

Add and subtract within 20.
1.OA.C.6 Add and subtract within 20, demonstrating fluency for addition and subtraction within 10. Use strategies such as counting on; making ten (e.g., $8 + 6 = 8 + 2 + 4 = 10 + 4 = 14$); decomposing a number leading to a ten (e.g., $13 - 4 = 13 - 3 - 1 = 10 - 1 = 9$);

using the relationship between addition and subtraction (e.g., knowing that $8 + 4 = 12$, one knows $12 - 8 = 4$); and creating equivalent but easier or known sums (e.g., adding $6 + 7$ by creating the known equivalent $6 + 6 + 1 = 12 + 1 = 13$).

Lesson Objective
Use objects to subtract one and find the difference.

Essential Question
How can you use objects to subtract one?

Materials
MathBoard, connecting cubes

 GO DIGITAL

📺 Animated Math Models
ⓘ *i*Tools: Counters

 **TEACH and TALK** *Animated Math Models*

Materials connecting cubes

Show children a ten-cube train and draw the cube train on the board. Explain that you are going to remove one cube. Remove the cube. Circle and mark an X on the cube on the right to show the cube you removed. Write the subtraction sentence $10 - 1 = 9$.

2 PRACTICE 📝 MATH BOARD

Materials connecting cubes

Explain that in this lesson children must trace the *minus* symbol and the *is equal to* symbol in each exercise.

PG60 Planning Guide

This lesson builds on the concept of subtraction presented in Chapter 6 and prepares children for the concept of counting back taught in Grade 1.

Name _____

Subtract One

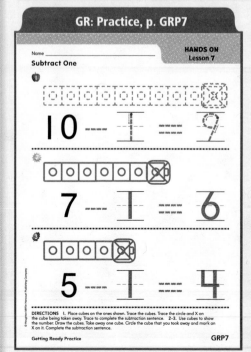

DIRECTIONS 1. Place cubes on the ones shown. Trace the cubes. Trace the circle and X on the cube being taken away. Trace to complete the subtraction sentence. 2–3. Use cubes to show the number. Draw the cubes. Take away one cube. Circle the cube that you took away and mark an X on it. Complete the subtraction sentence.

Getting Ready for Grade 1 fifteen **GR15**

GR: Practice, p. GRP7

Name _____ **HANDS ON Lesson 7**

Subtract One

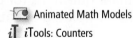

$10 - 1 = 9$

$7 - 1 = 6$

$5 - 1 = 4$

DIRECTIONS 1. Place cubes on the ones shown. Trace the cubes. Trace the circle and X on the cube being taken away. Trace to complete the subtraction sentence. 2–3. Use cubes to show the number. Draw the cubes. Take away one cube. Circle the cube that you took away and mark an X on it. Complete the subtraction sentence.

Getting Ready Practice **GRP7**

GR: Reteach, p. GRR7

Name _____ Lesson 7 Reteach

Subtract One

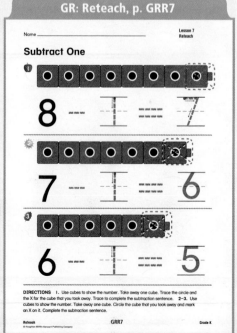

DIRECTIONS 1. Use cubes to show the number. Take away one cube. Trace the circle and the X for the cube that you took away. Trace to complete the subtraction sentence. 2–3. Use cubes to show the number. Take away one cube. Circle the cube that you took away and mark an X on it. Complete the subtraction sentence.

Reteach **GRR7** Grade K

---

*GR – Getting Ready Lessons and Resources (*www.thinkcentral.com*)

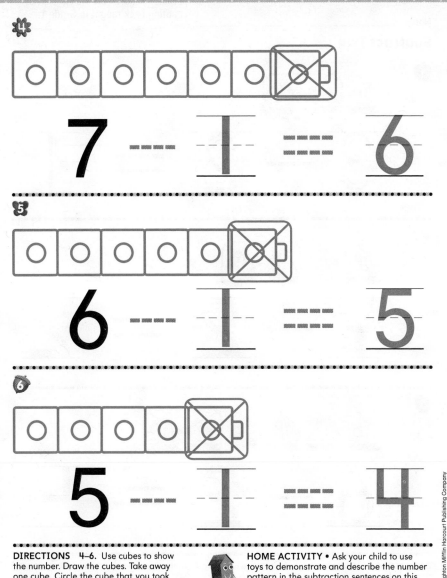

4

$$7 - 1 = 6$$

5

$$6 - 1 = 5$$

6

$$5 - 1 = 4$$

DIRECTIONS 4–6. Use cubes to show the number. Draw the cubes. Take away one cube. Circle the cube that you took away and mark an X on it. Complete the subtraction sentence.

HOME ACTIVITY • Ask your child to use toys to demonstrate and describe the number pattern in the subtraction sentences on this page.

GR16 sixteen

Have children locate Exercise 1.

- **How many cubes are there in all?** 10
- **Place cubes on the ones shown. How many cubes are taken away?** 1
- **Take away one cube. Trace the circle and the X over the cube on the page to show you took it away. How many cubes are left?** 9
- **Trace the numbers to complete the subtraction sentence.**

Read the subtraction sentence with children.

Have children locate Exercise 2.

- **How many cubes are there in all?** 9
- **Place and draw the cubes. How many cubes are taken away?** 1
- **Draw a circle around the last cube and mark an X on it. How many cubes are left?** 8
- **Trace and write to complete the subtraction sentence.**

Repeat the process with Exercises 3–6.

3 SUMMARIZE

 **MATHEMATICAL PRACTICES**

Essential Question

How can you use objects to subtract one?

I can use objects to show how many in all. Then I can remove the cube being taken away and count how many are left.

Math Journal  Math

Draw 4 cubes. Circle one cube to show it is taken away. Mark an X on it. Write how many cubes are left.

Subtract Two

LESSON AT A GLANCE

Common Core Standards
Understand addition as putting together and adding to, and understand subtraction as taking apart and taking from.
K.OA.A.1 Represent addition and subtraction with objects, fingers, mental images, drawings, sounds (e.g., claps), acting out situations, verbal explanations, expressions, or equations.

Add and subtract within 20.
1.OA.C.6 Add and subtract within 20, demonstrating fluency for addition and subtraction within 10. Use strategies such as counting on; making ten (e.g., $8 + 6 = 8 + 2 + 4 = 10 + 4 = 14$); decomposing a number leading to a ten (e.g., $13 - 4 = 13 - 3 - 1 = 10 - 1 = 9$);

using the relationship between addition and subtraction (e.g., knowing that $8 + 4 = 12$, one knows $12 - 8 = 4$); and creating equivalent but easier or known sums (e.g., adding $6 + 7$ by creating the known equivalent $6 + 6 + 1 = 12 + 1 = 13$).

Lesson Objective
Use pictures to subtract two and find the difference.

Essential Question
How can you subtract two?

Materials
MathBoard

 Animated Math Models
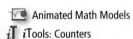 iTools: Counters

1 TEACH and TALK  Animated Math Models

Draw 5 apples on the board.

Write the following subtraction sentence on the board:

$5 - 2 = $ ___

- **Look at the subtraction sentence. How many apples do you take away?** 2

Circle two of the apples on the board and mark them with an X.

- **How many apples are left?** 3

Write the number 3 to complete the subtraction sentence.

This lesson builds on the concept of subtraction presented in Chapter 6 and prepares children for the concept of counting back taught in Grade 1.

Name _____

Subtract Two

$3 - 2 = 1$

$4 - 2 = 2$

$6 - 2 = 4$

DIRECTIONS 1. Count how many boats there are in all. Trace the circle and the X that shows the boats that sail away. Trace to complete the subtraction sentence. 2–3. Count how many boats there are in all. Two boats sail away. Circle the boats that sail away. Mark an X on them. Complete the subtraction sentence.

Getting Ready for Grade 1   seventeen **GR17**

GR: Practice, p. GRP8

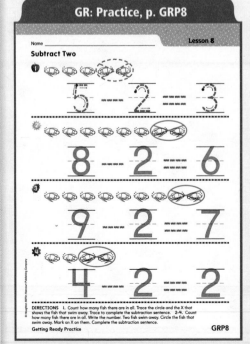

GR: Reteach, p. GRR8

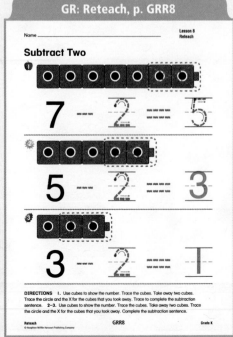

*GR – Getting Ready Lessons and Resources (*www.thinkcentral.com*)

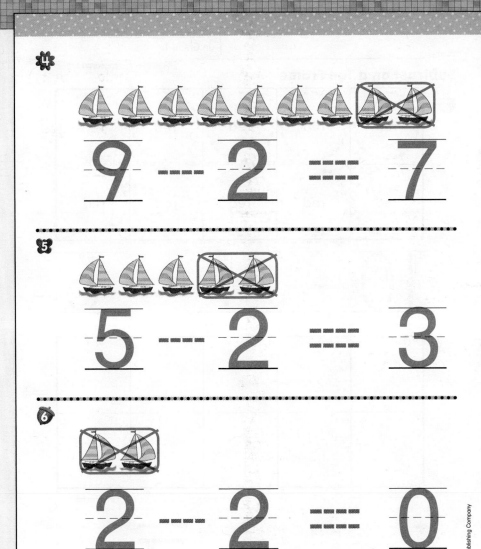

4

$$9 - 2 = 7$$

5

$$5 - 2 = 3$$

6

$$2 - 2 = 0$$

DIRECTIONS 4–6. Count how many boats there are in all. Write the number. Two boats sail away. Circle the boats that sail away. Mark an X on them. Complete the subtraction sentence.

HOME ACTIVITY • Give your child five buttons. Have your child take away two buttons and tell how many are left.

© Houghton Mifflin Harcourt Publishing Company

GR18 eighteen

---

2 PRACTICE

Have children locate Exercise 1.

- **Look at the first number. This number shows how many boats in all. Trace the number. How many boats are being taken away?** 2
- **Trace the circle and the X on the boats being taken away. How many boats are left?** 1
- **Trace to complete the subtraction sentence.**

Have children locate Exercise 2.

- **How many boats are there in all? Write the number.** 4
- **How many boats sail away? Write the number.** 2
- **Circle those boats and mark an X on them. Write and trace to complete the subtraction sentence.**

Repeat the process with Exercises 3–6.

3 SUMMARIZE

MATHEMATICAL PRACTICES

Essential Question

How can you subtract two? I can look at the picture to know how many in all. Then I can circle the two being taken away and find how many are left.

Math Journal  Math

Draw 4 bugs. Circle 2 bugs that crawl away and mark an X on them. Write how many are left.

LESSON 9

Hands On • Subtract on a Ten Frame

LESSON AT A GLANCE

Common Core Standards
Understand addition as putting together and adding to, and understand subtraction as taking apart and taking from.
K.OA.A.1 Represent addition and subtraction with objects, fingers, mental images, drawings, sounds (e.g., claps), acting out situations, verbal explanations, expressions, or equations.

Add and subtract within 20.
1.OA.C.6 Add and subtract within 20, demonstrating fluency for addition and subtraction within 10. Use strategies such as counting on; making ten (e.g., $8 + 6 = 8 + 2 + 4 = 10 + 4 = 14$); decomposing a number leading to a ten (e.g., $13 - 4 = 13 - 3 - 1 = 10 - 1 = 9$);

using the relationship between addition and subtraction (e.g., knowing that $8 + 4 = 12$, one knows $12 - 8 = 4$); and creating equivalent but easier or known sums (e.g., adding $6 + 7$ by creating the known equivalent $6 + 6 + 1 = 12 + 1 = 13$).

Lesson Objective
Subtract from 10 on a ten frame.

Essential Question
How can you use a ten frame to subtract?

Materials
MathBoard, two-color counters

iTools: Counters
HMH Mega Math

1 TEACH and TALK
Animated Math Models

Materials Workmat 3 (ten frame) (see *eTeacher Resources*), two-color counters

Have children place 10 red counters in the ten frame.

- **How many red counters are there?** 10
- **Take three counters off the ten frame. How many counters are left in the ten frame?** 7
- **What subtraction sentence can you write to show this?** $10 - 3 = 7$

This lesson builds on the concept of subtraction presented in Chapter 6 and prepares children for the concept of subtraction skills and strategies taught in Grade 1.

Name _____

Lesson 9

Subtract on a Ten Frame

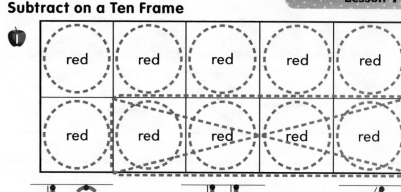

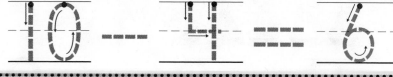

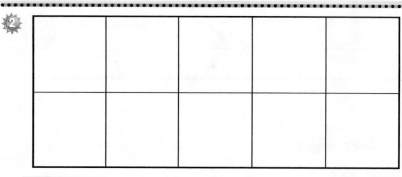

DIRECTIONS 1. Place 10 counters as shown on the ten frame. Take away 4 counters. Trace the circle around the set of counters that you took away. Trace the X on that set. Trace the subtraction sentence. 2. Place 10 counters on the ten frame. Draw the counters. Take away some counters. Circle the set of counters that you took away. Mark an X on that set. Complete the subtraction sentence.

Getting Ready for Grade 1

nineteen GRI9

GR: Practice, p. GRP9

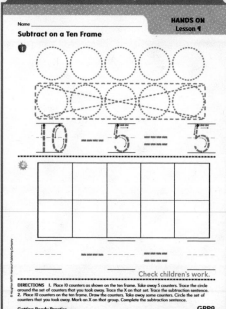

GR: Reteach, p. GRR9

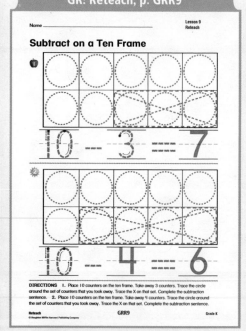

***GR** – Getting Ready Lessons and Resources (*www.thinkcentral.com*)

3

_____ _ _ _ _ = = = = _____ _____

Check children's work.

4

_ _ _ _ _ _ _ = = = = _____ _____

Check children's work.

DIRECTIONS 3–4. Place 10 counters on the ten frame. Draw the counters. Take away some counters. Circle the set of counters that you took away. Mark an X on that set. Complete the subtraction sentence.

GR20 twenty

HOME ACTIVITY • Give your child ten household objects, such as buttons. Have your child take some of the objects away. Then have him or her tell the subtraction sentence.

2 PRACTICE

Materials two-color counters

Have children look at Exercise 1.

- **Place 10 red counters in the ten frame as shown.**
- **How many counters are circled and marked with an X?** 4
- **Take away that many counters.**
- **How many counters are left in the ten frame?** 6
  Trace the subtraction sentence.

Have children complete Exercises 2–4, taking away a different set of counters for each exercise. Then have children complete the subtraction sentence to match the counters. Discuss the different subtraction facts for ten they modeled on the ten frame.

3 SUMMARIZE

MATHEMATICAL PRACTICES

Essential Question

How can you use a ten frame to subtract? I can place counters to fill the ten frame and then remove some. I know that the counters that remain in the ten frame show the amount left.

Math Journal  Math

Draw 10 counters. Circle 3 counters to show counters that are taken away. Mark an X on that set. Write how many counters are left.

LESSON 10

Algebra • Missing Part

LESSON AT A GLANCE

Common Core Standards
Understand addition as putting together and adding to, and understand subtraction as taking apart and taking from.
K.OA.A.1 Represent addition and subtraction with objects, fingers, mental images, drawings, sounds (e.g., claps), acting out situations, verbal explanations, expressions, or equations.

Add and subtract within 20.
1.OA.C.6 Add and subtract within 20, demonstrating fluency for addition and subtraction within 10. Use strategies such as counting on; making ten (e.g., $8 + 6 = 8 + 2 + 4 = 10 + 4 = 14$); decomposing a number leading to a ten (e.g., $13 - 4 = 13 - 3 - 1 = 10 - 1 = 9$);

using the relationship between addition and subtraction (e.g., knowing that $8 + 4 = 12$, one knows $12 - 8 = 4$); and creating equivalent but easier or known sums (e.g., adding $6 + 7$ by creating the known equivalent $6 + 6 + 1 = 12 + 1 = 13$).

Lesson Objective
Find the missing part that makes the whole in subtraction.

Essential Question
How can you find the missing part that makes the whole?

Materials
MathBoard

 GO DIGITAL iT *i*Tools: Counters
MM HMH Mega Math

1 TEACH and TALK **GO DIGITAL** • Animated Math Models

Materials connecting cubes

Show children an eight-cube train.

- **How many cubes are there?** 8
- **If I break apart two cubes, how many are left?** 6

Hold up the six-cube train.

- **How many cubes are in this cube train?** 6

Hold up the two-cube train.

- **How many cubes are in this cube train?** 2
- **What can you tell me about the number 8 and these two parts?** 8 is made up of two parts, 6 and 2.

PG66   Planning Guide

This lesson builds on the concept of subtraction presented in Chapter 6 and prepares children for the concept of decomposing numbers taught in Grade 1.

Name _____

Algebra: Missing Part

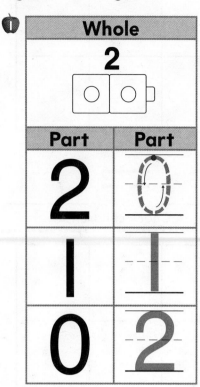

© Houghton Mifflin Harcourt Publishing Company

DIRECTIONS 1–2. How many cubes are there in all? Complete the chart to show the missing part that makes the whole.

Getting Ready for Grade 1   twenty-one **GR21**

GR: Practice, p. GRP10

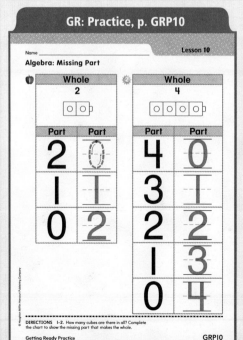

GR: Reteach, p. GRR10

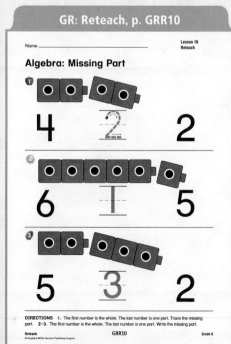

*GR – Getting Ready Lessons and Resources (*www.thinkcentral.com*)

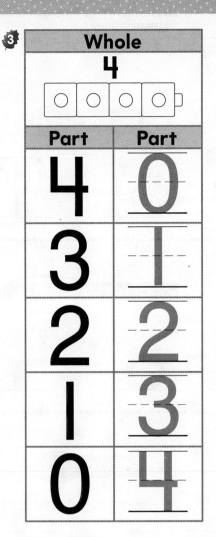

❸	Whole	
	4	
Part		Part
4		0
3		1
2		2
1		3
0		4

❹	Whole	
	5	
Part		Part
5		0
4		1
3		2
2		3
1		4
0		5

DIRECTIONS 3–4. How many cubes are there in all? Complete the chart to show the missing part that makes the whole.

GR22 twenty-two

HOME ACTIVITY • Place 8 spoons on the table. Cover 3 of the spoons. Tell your child that you started with 8 spoons. Ask him or her to tell you how many spoons are covered.

❷ **PRACTICE**

Have children look at Exercise 1. You may need to work with cubes to model the missing part.

- **How many cubes are there in all?** 2
- **If you have 2 cubes in one part of 2, how many cubes would be in the other part?** 0

Trace the number to show the missing part.

- **If you have 1 as one part of 2, what would the other part be?** 1

Write that number on your chart. Continue to write the other missing part that makes 2.

Have children complete Exercise 2 writing the missing part that makes 3.

Have children complete Exercises 3 and 4 in a similar way. Discuss the missing parts that make 4 and 5.

❸ **SUMMARIZE**

MATHEMATICAL PRACTICES

Essential Question

How can you find the missing part that makes the whole? I can look at the whole and break it apart to find the two parts that make the whole.

Math Journal

Draw a 2-cube train and a 3-cube train. Write the numbers that show these two parts of 5.

Related Subtraction Equations

LESSON AT A GLANCE

Common Core Standards

Understand addition as putting together and adding to, and understand subtraction as taking apart and taking from.

K.OA.A.1 Represent addition and subtraction with objects, fingers, mental images, drawings, sounds (e.g., claps), acting out situations, verbal explanations, expressions, or equations.

Add and subtract within 20.

1.OA.C.6 Add and subtract within 20, demonstrating fluency for addition and subtraction within 10. Use strategies such as counting on; making ten (e.g., $8 + 6 = 8 + 2 + 4 = 10 + 4 = 14$); decomposing a number leading to a ten (e.g., $13 - 4 = 13 - 3 - 1 = 10 - 1 = 9$);

using the relationship between addition and subtraction (e.g., knowing that $8 + 4 = 12$, one knows $12 - 8 = 4$); and creating equivalent but easier or known sums (e.g., adding $6 + 7$ by creating the known equivalent $6 + 6 + 1 = 12 + 1 = 13$).

Lesson Objective

Identify equivalent subtraction expressions.

Essential Question

How do you know if two different subtraction facts are equal?

Materials

MathBoard

 *i*Tools: Counters

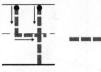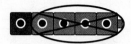

This lesson builds on basic subtraction concepts presented in Chapter 6 and prepares children for subtraction within 20 taught in Grade 1.

Name _____

Related Subtraction Equations

$$4 - 3 = 5 - 4$$

$$6 - 2 = 8 - 4$$

$$8 - 5 = 5 - 2$$

DIRECTIONS Look at the cube trains. 1. Trace to complete the equation. 2–3. Trace and write to complete the equation.

Getting Ready for Grade 1   twenty-three **GR23**

---

1 TEACH and TALK *Animated Math Models*

Materials connecting cubes

Show children a cube train with 3 red cubes and 1 blue cube.

- **I have 4 cubes, but I want 3. How many cubes do I need to break off?** 1 cube

Break off the blue cube and write $4 - 1$ on the board. Then show children a cube train with 3 red cubes and 2 blue cubes.

- **I have 5 cubes, but I want 3. How many cubes do I need to break off?** 2 cubes

Break off the 2 blue cubes and write $5 - 2$ on the board. Then hold up the two 3-cube trains that remain.

- **Is $4 - 1$ equal to $5 - 2$?** Yes, they are both 3.

On the board, add an *is equal to* symbol to show that $4 - 1 = 5 - 2$. Read the equation.

PG68   Planning Guide

GR: Practice, p. GRP11

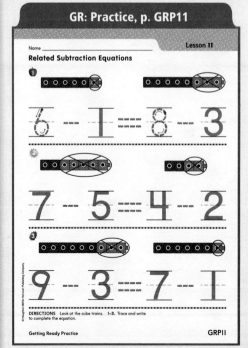

GR: Reteach, p. GRR11

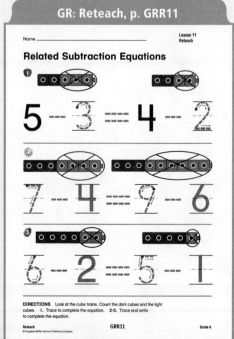

*GR – Getting Ready Lessons and Resources (*www.thinkcentral.com*)

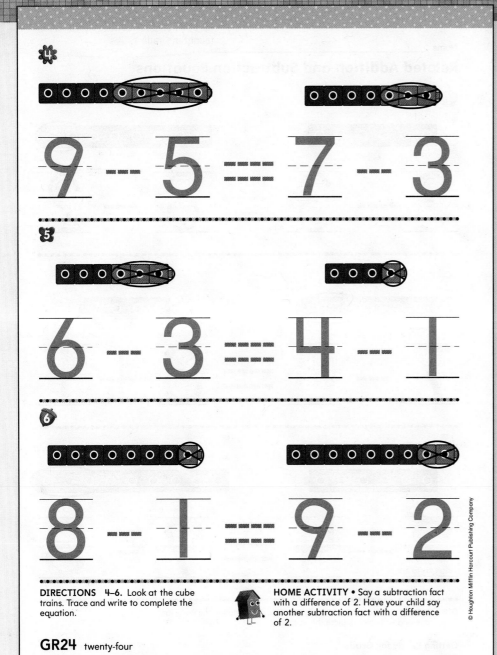

DIRECTIONS 4–6. Look at the cube trains. Trace and write to complete the equation.

HOME ACTIVITY • Say a subtraction fact with a difference of 2. Have your child say another subtraction fact with a difference of 2.

© Houghton Mifflin Harcourt Publishing Company

GR24 twenty-four

2 PRACTICE

Materials connecting cubes

Have children look at Exercise 1.

- **What subtraction fact does the first cube train show?** 4 − 3 = 1 **What subtraction fact does the second cube train show?** 5 − 4 = 1

- **Is 4 − 3 equal to 5 − 4?** Yes, they are both 1. **What equation shows they are equal?** 4 − 3 = 5 − 4

Have children trace the equation.

Have children locate Exercise 2.

- **What subtraction facts do the cube trains show?** 6 − 2 = 4 and 8 − 4 = 4

- **Is 6 − 2 equal to 8 − 4?** Yes, they are both 4. **What equation will you write to show they are equal?** 6 − 2 = 8 − 4

Continue with similar questions for Exercises 3–6. Then read the completed equations together as a class.

3 SUMMARIZE

MATHEMATICAL PRACTICES

Essential Question

How do you know if two different subtraction facts are equal? I can look at cube trains that show the subtraction facts. If the cube trains have the same number of cubes after the subtraction is done, the facts are equal.

Math Journal WRITE Math

You may want children to place these pages in a Math Journal.

LESSON 12

Related Addition and Subtraction Equations

LESSON AT A GLANCE

Common Core Standards
Understand addition as putting together and adding to, and understand subtraction as taking apart and taking from.
K.OA.A.1 Represent addition and subtraction with objects, fingers, mental images, drawings, sounds (e.g., claps), acting out situations, verbal explanations, expressions, or equations.

Add and subtract within 20.
1.OA.C.6 Add and subtract within 20, demonstrating fluency for addition and subtraction within 10. Use strategies such as counting on; making ten (e.g., 8 + 6 = 8 + 2 + 4 = 10 + 4 = 14); decomposing a number leading to a ten (e.g., 13 − 4 = 13 − 3 − 1 = 10 − 1 = 9);

using the relationship between addition and subtraction (e.g., knowing that 8 + 4 = 12, one knows 12 − 8 = 4); and creating equivalent but easier or known sums (e.g., adding 6 + 7 by creating the known equivalent 6 + 6 + 1 = 12 + 1 = 13).

Lesson Objective
Identify equivalent addition and subtraction expressions.

Essential Question
How do you know if an addition fact and a subtraction fact are equal?

Materials
MathBoard

1 TEACH and TALK

Materials connecting cubes

Show children a cube train with 2 red cubes and 1 blue cube.

- **My cube train shows 3. What did I add to make 3?** 2 and 1

Write 2 + 1 on the board. Then show children a cube train with 3 red cubes and 2 white cubes.

- **I want to make 3 again. How many cubes do I need to break off?** 2 cubes

- Break off the 2 white cubes and write 5 − 2 on the board. Then hold up the two 3-cube trains.

- **Is 2 + 1 equal to 5 − 2?** Yes, they are both 3.

On the board, add an *is equal to* symbol to show that 2 + 1 = 5 − 2. Read the equation.

Name _____

Related Addition and Subtraction Equations

This lesson builds on basic addition and subtraction concepts presented in Chapters 5–6 and prepares children for addition and subtraction within 20 taught in Grade 1.

❶

$$3 + 3 = 8 - 2$$

❷

$$7 - 3 = 3 + 1$$

❸

$$2 + 4 = 9 - 3$$

DIRECTIONS Look at the cube trains. 1. Trace to complete the equation. 2–3. Trace and write to complete the equation.

Getting Ready for Grade 1   twenty-five **GR25**

GR: Practice, p. GRP12

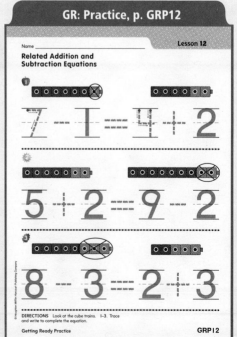

GR: Reteach, p. GRR12

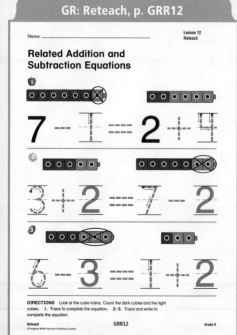

*GR – Getting Ready Lessons and Resources (*www.thinkcentral.com*)

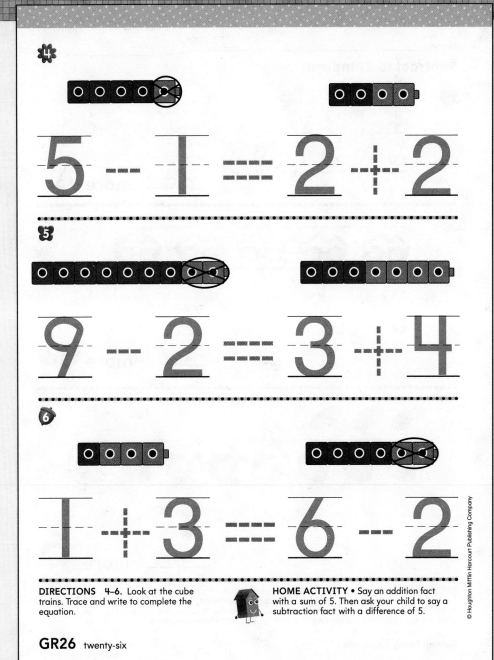

$$5 - 1 = 2 + 2$$

$$9 - 2 = 3 + 4$$

$$1 + 3 = 6 - 2$$

DIRECTIONS 4–6. Look at the cube trains. Trace and write to complete the equation.

HOME ACTIVITY • Say an addition fact with a sum of 5. Then ask your child to say a subtraction fact with a difference of 5.

© Houghton Mifflin Harcourt Publishing Company

GR26 twenty-six

End-of-Year Resources

② PRACTICE

Materials connecting cubes

Have children look at Exercise 1.

- **What addition fact does the first cube train show?** 3 + 3 = 6 **What subtraction fact does the second cube train show?** 8 − 2 = 6
- **Is 3 + 3 equal to 8 − 2?** Yes, they are both 6. **What equation shows they are equal?** 3 + 3 = 8 − 2

Have children trace the equation.

Have children locate Exercise 2.

- **What facts do the cube trains show?** 7 − 3 = 4 and 3 + 1 = 4
- **Is 7 − 3 equal to 3 + 1?** Yes, they are both 4. **What equation will you write to show they are equal?** 7 − 3 = 3 + 1

Continue with similar questions for Exercises 3–6. Then read the completed equations together as a class.

③ SUMMARIZE

Common Core MATHEMATICAL PRACTICES

Essential Question

How do you know if an addition fact and a subtraction fact are equal? I can look at cube trains that show the facts. If the cube trains have the same number of cubes after the addition and subtraction is done, the facts are equal.

Math Journal WRITE Math

You may want children to place these pages in a Math Journal.

LESSON 13

Subtract to Compare

LESSON AT A GLANCE

Common Core Standards

Understand addition as putting together and adding to, and understand subtraction as taking apart and taking from.

K.OA.A.1 Represent addition and subtraction with objects, fingers, mental images, drawings, sounds (e.g., claps), acting out situations, verbal explanations, expressions, or equations.

Add and subtract within 20.

1.OA.C.6 Add and subtract within 20, demonstrating fluency for addition and subtraction within 10. Use strategies such as counting on; making ten (e.g., $8 + 6 = 8 + 2 + 4 = 10 + 4 = 14$); decomposing a number leading to a ten (e.g., $13 - 4 = 13 - 3 - 1 = 10 - 1 = 9$);

using the relationship between addition and subtraction (e.g., knowing that $8 + 4 = 12$, one knows $12 - 8 = 4$); and creating equivalent but easier or known sums (e.g., adding $6 + 7$ by creating the known equivalent $6 + 6 + 1 = 12 + 1 = 13$).

Lesson Objective
Match objects in sets to compare quantities.

Essential Question
How can you compare sets of objects?

Materials
MathBoard

GO DIGITAL
- Animated Math Models
- **iT** iTools: Counters
- **MM** HMH Mega Math: Numberopolis

1 TEACH and TALK **GO DIGITAL** • Animated Math Models

Have 5 girls stand in the front of the room. Then have 3 boys stand in the front of the room. Have each boy stand in front of one of the girls.

- **We have a group of girls and a group of boys. Are there more boys or girls?** girls
- **How do you know?** The boys and girls are lined up and I can see that there are some girls that do not have a partner.
- **How many more girls are there than boys?** 2

Explain that by matching groups of objects it is easy to see which group has more.

This lesson builds on the concept of subtraction presented in Chapter 6 and prepares children for the concept of comparative subtraction taught in Grade 1.

Name _____

Subtract to Compare

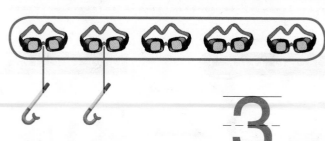

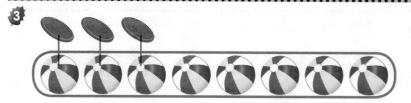

DIRECTIONS 1. Trace the lines to match the objects in the top row to the objects in the bottom row. Compare the sets. Trace the circle that shows the set with more objects. Trace the number. 2–3. Draw lines to match the objects in the top row to the objects in the bottom row. Compare the sets. Circle the set that has more objects. Write how many more.

Getting Ready for Grade 1   twenty-seven **GR27**

GR: Practice, p. GRP13

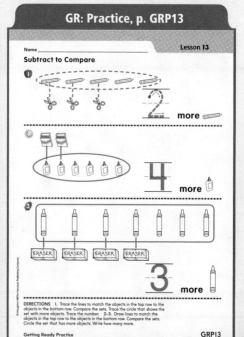

GR: Reteach, p. GRR13

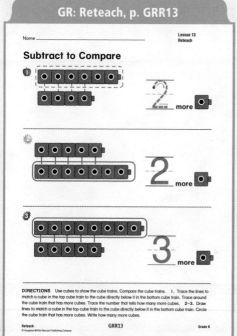

*GR – Getting Ready Lessons and Resources (*www.thinkcentral.com*)

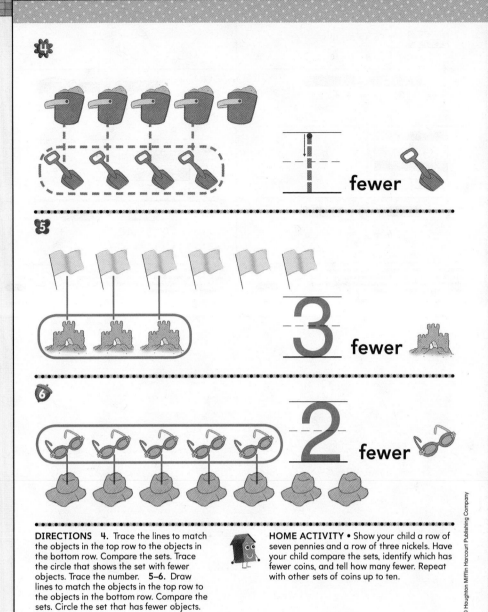

DIRECTIONS 4. Trace the lines to match the objects in the top row to the objects in the bottom row. Compare the sets. Trace the circle that shows the set with fewer objects. Trace the number. **5–6.** Draw lines to match the objects in the top row to the objects in the bottom row. Compare the sets. Circle the set that has fewer objects. Write how many fewer.

HOME ACTIVITY • Show your child a row of seven pennies and a row of three nickels. Have your child compare the sets, identify which has fewer coins, and tell how many fewer. Repeat with other sets of coins up to ten.

© Houghton Mifflin Harcourt Publishing Company

GR28 twenty-eight

Getting Ready Lessons and Resources, pp. GR29–GR30   ✔ Checkpoint

Name _____

✔ **Checkpoint**

Concepts and Skills

2

Check children's work.

DIRECTIONS 1. Use cubes to show the number. Draw the cubes. Take away one cube. Circle the cube that you took away and mark an X on it. Complete the subtraction sentence. **2.** Place 10 counters on the ten frame. Draw the counters. Take away some counters. Circle and mark an X on the counters that you took away. Complete the subtraction sentence.

Getting Ready for Grade K   twenty-nine **GR29**

© Houghton Mifflin Harcourt Publishing Company

---

7 – 2 = 5

4 + 4   6 + 2

2   3   4   5
○   ●   ○   ○

DIRECTIONS 3. Count and write how many boats in all. Two boats leave. Circle and mark an X on those boats. Complete the subtraction sentence. **4.** Look at the cube trains. Trace and write to complete the equation. **5.** Compare the sets. Mark under the number that shows how many more dogs are shown in the picture.

GR30 thirty

© Houghton Mifflin Harcourt Publishing Company

---

2 PRACTICE   MATH BOARD

Have children locate Exercise 1.
- **Trace the lines to match the objects in the top row to the objects in the bottom row.**
- **Trace the circle around the set that has more objects. Trace the number that shows how many more.**

In Exercises 2 and 3 have children draw lines to match the objects in the top row to the objects in the bottom row. Have children compare the sets and circle the set that has more objects. Then have them write the number that shows how many more.

Have children locate Exercise 4.
- **Trace the lines to match the objects in the top row to the objects in the bottom row.**
- **Trace the circle around the set that has fewer objects. Trace the number that shows how many fewer.**

Have children complete Exercises 5 and 6 by drawing lines to match the objects in the top row to the objects in the bottom row. Have them compare the sets and circle the set that has fewer objects. Then have them write the number that shows how many fewer.

3 SUMMARIZE

Common Core **MATHEMATICAL PRACTICES**

Essential Question

How can you compare sets of objects? I can compare sets of objects by drawing lines to see which set has more or fewer.

Math Journal    Math

Draw 4 shoes and 2 socks. Circle the set with more objects. Write how many more.

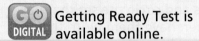

Getting Ready for Grade 1
Test

LESSONS 1 TO 13

Summative Assessment

Use the **Getting Ready Test** to assess children's progress in Getting Ready for Grade 1 Lessons 1–13.

Getting Ready Tests are provided in multiple-choice and mixed-response format in the *Getting Ready Lessons and Resources*.

GO DIGITAL Getting Ready Test is available online.

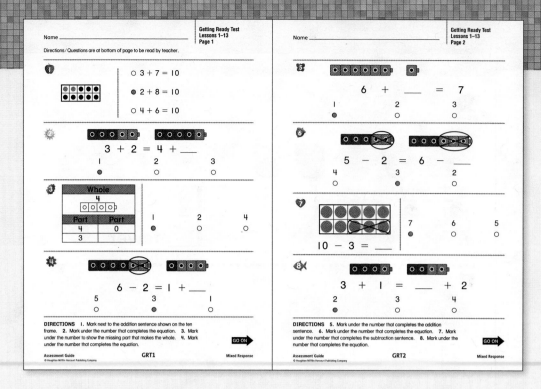

✓ Data-Driven Decision Making ▲ RtI

Item	Lesson	Common Error	Intervene With
1	3	May not understand how to add to 10 on a ten frame	**R**—p. GRR3
2, 8	6	May not understand how addition sentences are related	**R**—p. GRR6
3	4	May not understand how number pairs make a number	**R**—p. GRR4
4	12	May not understand how addition and subtraction equations are related	**R**—p. GRR12
5, 12	1	May not understand how to count forward 1	**R**—p. GRR1
6	11	May not understand how subtraction equations are related	**R**—p. GRR11

Key: R—Getting Ready Lessons and Resources: Reteach

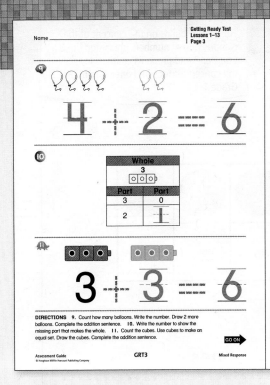

Portfolio Suggestions The portfolio represents the growth, talents, achievements, and reflections of the mathematics learner. Children might spend a short time selecting work samples for their portfolios.

You may want to have children respond to the following questions:

• Which question was difficult?
• What would you like to learn more about?

For information about how to organize, share, and evaluate portfolios, see the *Chapter Resources*.

✔ Data-Driven Decision Making ▲ RtI

Item	Lesson	Common Error	Intervene With
7	9	May not understand how to use a ten frame to subtract	R—p. GRR9
9	2	May not understand how to count forward 2	R—p. GRR2
10	10	May not understand how number pairs make a number	R—p. GRR10
11	5	May not recognize equal sets	R—p. GRR5
13	8	May not understand how to subtract 2	R—p. GRR8
14	13	May not understand how to compare sets	R—p. GRR13
15	7	May not understand how to subtract 1	R—p. GRR7

Key: R—Getting Ready Lessons and Resources: Reteach

LESSON 14

Hands On • How Many Ones?

LESSON AT A GLANCE

Common Core Standards
Know number names and the count sequence.
K.CC.A.1 Count to 100 by ones and by tens.

Extend the counting sequence.
1.NBT.A.1 Count to 120, starting at any number less than 120. In this range, read and write numerals and represent a number of objects with a written numeral.

Lesson Objective
Understand that numbers less than 10 are called ones.

Essential Question
How can you count numbers less than 10 by ones?

Materials
MathBoard, two-color counters

 *i*Tools: Counters

1 TEACH and TALK · Animated Math Models

Materials two-color counters, Workmat 3 (ten frame) (see *eTeacher Resources*)

Have children place 4 counters in the ten frame.
- **How many counters are in the ten frame?** 4
- **How many ones are there?** 4
- **How many more counters do you need to make 10?** 6

2 PRACTICE

Materials two-color counters

Have children locate Exercise 1.
- **How many counters will you place in the ten frame?** 6
- **How many ones is that?** 6
- **Write the number that shows how many ones.**

This lesson builds on the concept of the composition of numbers presented in Chapter 7 and prepares children for the concept of tens and ones taught in Grade 1.

Name _____

Hands On: How Many Ones?

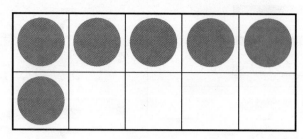

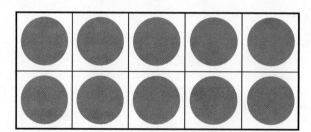

_____ ones   or   _____ ten

DIRECTIONS Place counters on the ones shown. **1.** How many ones are there? Write the number. **2.** How many ones are there? Write the number. How many tens is that? Write the number.

Getting Ready for Grade 1

thirty-one **GR31**

© Houghton Mifflin Harcourt Publishing Company

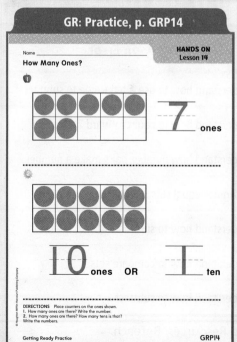
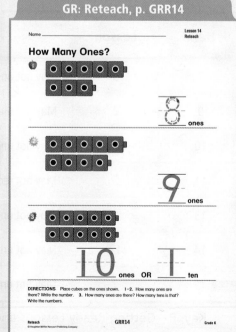
*GR – Getting Ready Lessons and Resources (*www.thinkcentral.com*)

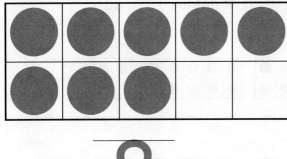

_____
8 ones

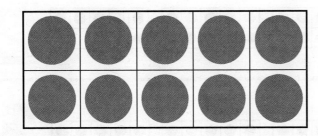

_____
10 ones   or   _____
1 ten

DIRECTIONS Place counters on the ones shown. **3.** How many ones are there? Write the number. **4.** How many ones are there? How many tens is that? Write the number.

HOME ACTIVITY • Place 10 small items on a table. Ask your child to count and write how many ones that is. Then ask him or her to write how many tens that is.

GR32 thirty-two

When children get to Exercise 2 make sure they are aware that 10 can be thought of as a group of ones—a unit called a "ten." Remind children that 10 ones is also 1 ten. Have children complete Exercise 2 by placing counters on the ones shown in the ten frame. Ask similar questions as in Exercise 1.

Have children complete Exercises 3 and 4 in a similar way. Have children say how many ones. When they get to Exercise 4, ask how many ones, and how many tens.

3 SUMMARIZE

 **MATHEMATICAL PRACTICES**

Essential Question

How can you count numbers less than 10 by ones? I say one number for each object counted. I know that numbers less than 10 are counted as ones.

Math Journal   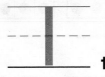 Math

Draw a group of 10 counters. Write how many ones and how many tens.

LESSON 15

Read and Write Numbers 20 to 30

LESSON AT A GLANCE

Common Core Standards
Know number names and the count sequence.
K.CC.A.1 Count to 100 by ones and by tens.

Extend the counting sequence.
1.NBT.A.1 Count to 120, starting at any number less than 120. In this range, read and write numerals and represent a number of objects with a written numeral.

Lesson Objective
Use written and spoken numbers 20 to 30 to describe counters pictured in ten frames.

Essential Question
How can you read and write numbers 20 to 30?

Materials
MathBoard

iT iTools: Counters
MM HMH Mega Math

1 TEACH and TALK 🔵 *Animated Math Models*

Materials counters or iTools: Counters

Place counters on a surface, one at a time, as children count aloud with you. Stop after 10 counters.

- **How many are there so far?** 10

Place another group of 10 counters on the surface as children continue counting aloud, 11 to 20.

- **How many are there now?** 20

Place another group of 10 counters on the surface as children continue counting aloud, 21 to 30.

- **How many counters are there in all?** 30

This lesson builds on reading and writing numbers to 20 presented in Chapters 7–8 and prepares children for reading and writing numbers to 120 taught in Grade 1.

Name _____

Read and Write Numbers 20 to 30

DIRECTIONS How many counters are there? I. Trace the number. 2–5. Write the number.

Getting Ready for Grade I   thirty-three **GR33**

GR: Practice, p. GRP15

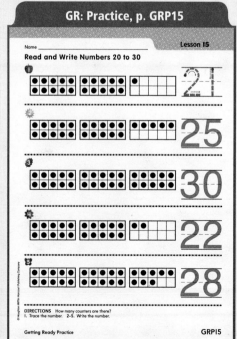

GR: Reteach, p. GRR15

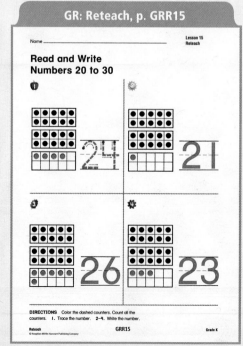

***GR** – Getting Ready Lessons and Resources (www.thinkcentral.com)

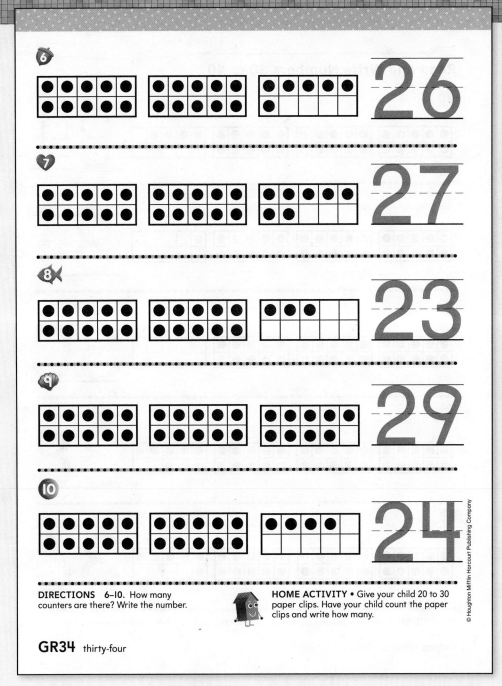

DIRECTIONS 6–10. How many counters are there? Write the number.

HOME ACTIVITY • Give your child 20 to 30 paper clips. Have your child count the paper clips and write how many.

GR34 thirty-four

② PRACTICE

Have children locate Exercise 1. Explain that they need to write the number of counters. They can count one by one, but it is faster to use the ten frames to help.

- **How many counters are in the first ten frame?** 10 **How many counters are in the next ten frame?** 10
- **How many counters are there so far?** 20
- **How many counters are in the last ten frame?** 2
- **How many counters are there in all?** 22

Have children trace the number.

Have children locate Exercise 2.

- **How many counters are in the first two ten frames?** 20
- **How many counters are in the last ten frame?** 5
- **How many counters are there in all?** 25 **How do you write 25?** 2 followed by 5

Continue with similar questions for Exercises 3–10. Then have children read aloud the numbers they wrote.

③ SUMMARIZE

 **MATHEMATICAL PRACTICES**

Essential Question

How can you read and write numbers 20 to 30? Except for thirty, the numbers start with 2 and end with another number 0 to 9. To read the number, I say twenty and then the other number.

Math Journal   WRITE Math

Draw 10 counters. Draw another 10 counters. Then draw 3 more counters. Write the number.

LESSON 16

Read and Write Numbers 30 to 40

LESSON AT A GLANCE

Common Core Standards
Know number names and the count sequence.
K.CC.A.1 Count to 100 by ones and by tens.

Extend the counting sequence.
1.NBT.A.1 Count to 120, starting at any number less than 120. In this range, read and write numerals and represent a number of objects with a written numeral.

Lesson Objective
Use written and spoken numbers 30 to 40 to describe counters pictured in ten frames.

Essential Question
How can you read and write numbers 30 to 40?

Materials
MathBoard

1 TEACH and TALK 🔲 * Animated Math Models

Materials counters or *iTools*: Counters

Place counters on a surface, one at a time, as children count aloud with you. Stop after 10 counters.

• **How many are there so far?** 10

Place another group of 10 counters on the surface as children continue counting aloud, 11 to 20.

• **How many are there so far?** 20

Place another group of 10 counters on the surface as children continue counting aloud, 21 to 30.

• **How many are there now?** 30

Place another group of 10 counters on the surface as children continue counting aloud, 31 to 40.

• **How many counters are there in all?** 40

Name _____

Read and Write Numbers 30 to 40

❶ **34**

❷ **31**

❸ **30**

❹ **38**

❺ **36**

DIRECTIONS How many counters are there? 1. Trace the number. 2–5. Write the number.

Getting Ready for Grade 1   thirty-five **GR35**

This lesson builds on reading and writing numbers to 20 presented in Chapters 7–8 and prepares children for reading and writing numbers to 120 taught in Grade 1.

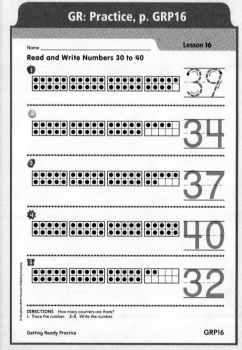

GR: Practice, p. GRP16

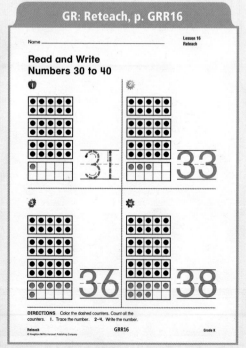

GR: Reteach, p. GRR16

---

*GR – Getting Ready Lessons and Resources (*www.thinkcentral.com*)

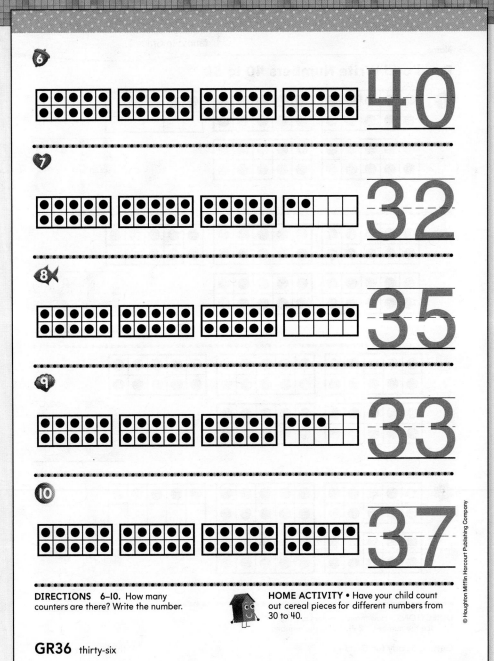

6. 40

7. 32

8. 35

9. 33

10. 37

DIRECTIONS 6–10. How many counters are there? Write the number.

HOME ACTIVITY • Have your child count out cereal pieces for different numbers from 30 to 40.

© Houghton Mifflin Harcourt Publishing Company

GR36 thirty-six

---

2 PRACTICE

Have children locate Exercise 1. Explain that children need to write the number of counters. They can count one by one, but it is faster to use the ten frames to help.

- **How many counters are in the first ten frame?** 10 **How many counters are in the next ten frame?** 10 **How many counters are in the next ten frame?** 10
- **How many counters are there so far?** 30
- **How many counters are in the last ten frame?** 4
- **How many counters are there in all?** 34

Have children trace the number.

Have children locate Exercise 2.

- **How many counters are in the first three ten frames?** 30
- **How many counters are in the last ten frame?** 1
- **How many counters are there in all?** 31 **How do you write 31?** 3 followed by 1

Continue with similar questions for Exercises 3–10. Then have children read aloud the numbers they wrote.

3 SUMMARIZE

MATHEMATICAL PRACTICES

Essential Question

How can you read and write numbers 30 to 40? Except for forty, the numbers start with 3 and end with another number 0 to 9. To read the number, I say thirty and then the other number.

Math Journal WRITE Math

Draw 10 counters. Draw another 10 counters. Draw 10 more counters. Then draw 2 more counters. Write the number.

LESSON 17

Read and Write Numbers 40 to 50

LESSON AT A GLANCE

Common Core Standards
Know number names and the count sequence.
K.CC.A.1 Count to 100 by ones and by tens.

Extend the counting sequence.
1.NBT.A.1 Count to 120, starting at any number less than 120. In this range, read and write numerals and represent a number of objects with a written numeral.

Lesson Objective
Use written and spoken numbers 40 to 50 to describe counters pictured in ten frames.

Essential Question
How can you read and write numbers 40 to 50?

Materials
MathBoard

1 TEACH and TALK

Materials counters

Place counters on a surface, one at a time, as children count aloud with you. Stop after 10 counters.

• **How many are there so far?** 10

Place another group of 10 counters on the surface as children continue counting, 11 to 20.

• **How many are there now?** 20

Place another group of 10 counters on the surface as children continue counting, 21 to 30.

• **How many are there now?** 30

Place another group of 10 counters on the surface as children continue counting, 31 to 40.

• **How many are there now?** 40

Place another group of 10 counters on the surface as children continue counting, 41 to 50.

• **How many counters are there in all?** 50

This lesson builds on reading and writing numbers to 20 presented in Chapters 7–8 and prepares children for reading and writing numbers to 120 taught in Grade 1.

Name _____

Read and Write Numbers 40 to 50

1. 43

2. 48

3. 50

4. 45

© Houghton Mifflin Harcourt Publishing Company

DIRECTIONS How many counters are there?
1. Trace the number.   2–4. Write the number.

Getting Ready for Grade 1

thirty-seven **GR37**

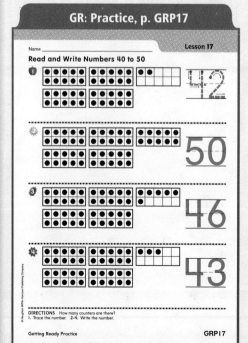

GR: Practice, p. GRP17

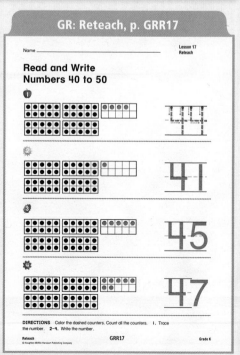

GR: Reteach, p. GRR17

*GR – Getting Ready Lessons and Resources (*www.thinkcentral.com*)

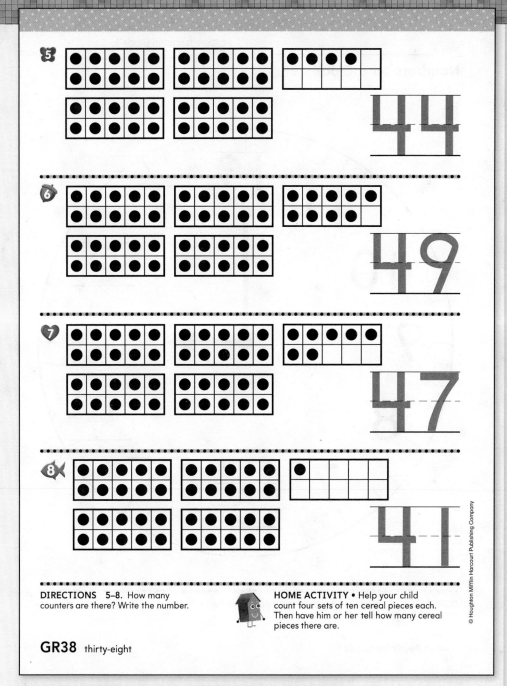

DIRECTIONS 5–8. How many counters are there? Write the number.

HOME ACTIVITY • Help your child count four sets of ten cereal pieces each. Then have him or her tell how many cereal pieces there are.

© Houghton Mifflin Harcourt Publishing Company

GR38 thirty-eight

Getting Ready Lessons and Resources, pp. GR39–GR40   ✓ **Checkpoint**

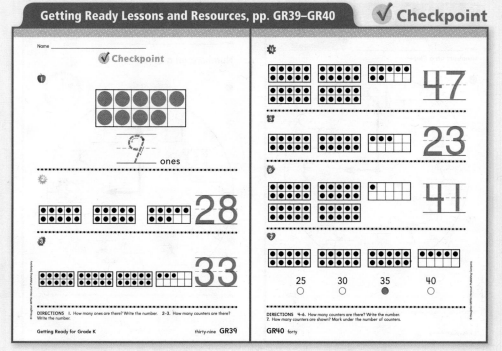

2 PRACTICE [MATH BOARD]

Have children locate Exercise 1. Explain that children need to write the number of counters. They can count one by one, but it is faster to use the ten frames to help.

- **How many counters are in each ten frame?** 10 **How many counters are in the first 4 ten frames?** 40
- **How many counters are in the last ten frame?** 3
- **How many counters are there in all?** 43

Have children trace the number.

Have children locate Exercise 2.

- **How many counters are in the first four ten frames?** 40
- **How many counters are in the last ten frame?** 8
- **How many counters are there in all?** 48 **How do you write 48?** 4 followed by 8

Continue with similar questions for Exercises 3–8. Then have children read aloud the numbers they wrote.

3 SUMMARIZE

[Common Core] MATHEMATICAL PRACTICES

Essential Question

How can you read and write numbers 40 to 50? Except for fifty, the numbers start with 4 and end with another number 0 to 9. To read the number, I say forty and then the other number.

Math Journal [WRITE Math]

You may want children to place these pages in a Math Journal.

This lesson builds on writing numbers to 20 presented in Chapters 7–8 and prepares children for telling and writing time taught in Grade 1.

LESSON 18

Numbers on a Clock

LESSON AT A GLANCE

Common Core Standards
Know number names and the count sequence.
K.CC.A.3 Write numbers from 0 to 20. Represent a number of objects with a written numeral 0–20 (with 0 representing a count of no objects).

Tell and write time.
1.MD.B.3 Tell and write time in hours and half-hours using analog and digital clocks.

Lesson Objective
Write numbers in the correct positions on a diagram of an analog clock.

Essential Question
How can you write the numbers on a clock?

Materials
MathBoard

1 TEACH and TALK

Materials *iTools:* Measurement (or use a teaching clock)

Position the hour hand of the analog clock at 1.

- **Where is the short hand pointing?** to the 1

Have children count aloud with you from 1 to 6 as you move the hour hand from number to number.

- **Where is the short hand pointing now?** to the 6 **Where is 6 on a clock?** at the bottom

Have children continue counting aloud with you to 12 as you move the hour hand from number to number.

- **Where is the short hand pointing now?** to the 12 **Where is 12 on a clock?** at the top

- **What happens next?** The hand goes around from 1 to 12 again and again.

Name _____

Numbers on a Clock

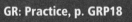

DIRECTIONS I. Trace 12 at the top of the clock. Write the numbers I to 6 in order on the clock.

Getting Ready for Grade I   forty-one **GR41**

© Houghton Mifflin Harcourt Publishing Company

GR: Practice, p. GRP18

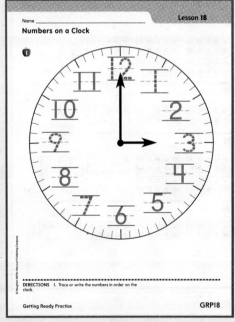

GR: Reteach, p. GRR18

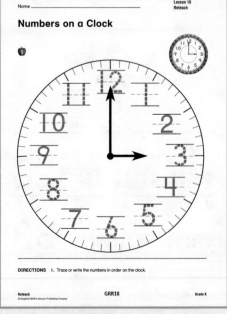

---

*GR – Getting Ready Lessons and Resources (*www.thinkcentral.com*)

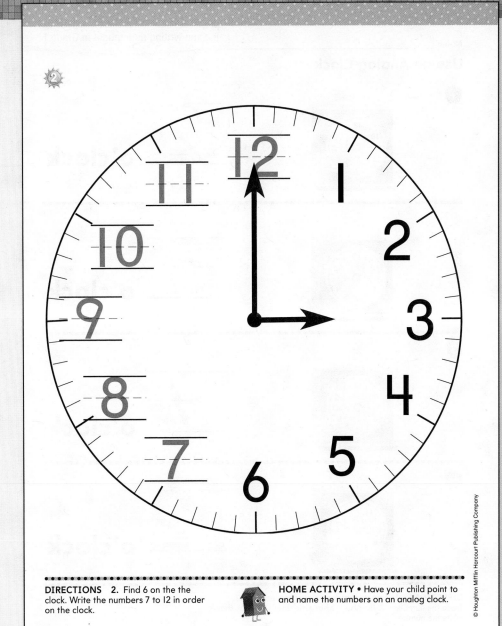

DIRECTIONS   2. Find 6 on the the clock. Write the numbers 7 to 12 in order on the clock.

HOME ACTIVITY • Have your child point to and name the numbers on an analog clock.

GR42   forty-two

© Houghton Mifflin Harcourt Publishing Company

2 PRACTICE

Have children locate the clock face on the first lesson page.

• **Where is 12 on a clock?** at the top

Have children trace number 12.

• **What number comes next after 12 on a clock?** 1 **Where will you write 1?** in the blank next to 12

Have children write 1. Continue with similar questions until children have written all the missing numbers.

Have children look at the clock face on the second lesson page.

• **Find 6. Where is 6 on a clock?** at the bottom

• **What number comes after 6?** 7 **Where will you write 7?** in the blank next to 6

Continue with similar questions until children have written all the missing numbers. Then have children point to the numbers and read them aloud from 1 to 12.

3 SUMMARIZE

Common Core **MATHEMATICAL PRACTICES**

Essential Question

How can you write the numbers on a clock?

I write 12 at the top. Then I start with 1 and number in order around the clock until I get to the 12.

Math Journal  Math

You may want children to place these pages in a Math Journal.

LESSON 19

Use an Analog Clock

LESSON AT A GLANCE

Common Core Standards
Know number names and the count sequence.
K.CC.A.3 Write numbers from 0 to 20. Represent a number of objects with a written numeral 0–20 (with 0 representing a count of no objects).

Tell and write time.
1.MD.B.3 Tell and write time in hours and half-hours using analog and digital clocks.

Lesson Objective
Use a clock to tell time.

Essential Question
How can you use a clock to tell time?

Materials
MathBoard

GO DIGITAL

▭✓ Animated Math Models
iT iTools: Measurement
〰 HMH Mega Math

1 TEACH and TALK GO DIGITAL · Animated Math Models

Materials classroom clock

Display a clock. Explain that a clock is a tool that measures time. Point to the numbers in order and ask children to count with you. Tell children that the shorter hand is the hour hand, and the longer hand is the minute hand.

Move the hour hand to each number of the clock, modeling the time as *about (1) o'clock*. Ask children to repeat each time.

- **How do the numbers help you know the time?** When the hour hand points to a number, you know what hour it is.
- **If it is about 7 o'clock, where will the hour hand be pointing?** to the number 7
- **Where will the hour hand point if it is before 7 o'clock?** before the number 7
- **Where will the hour hand point if it is after 7 o'clock?** after the number 7

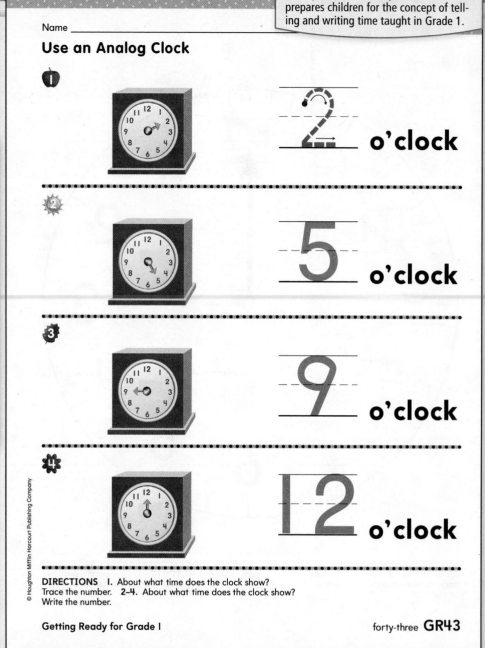

Name _____

Use an Analog Clock

DIRECTIONS 1. About what time does the clock show? Trace the number. 2–4. About what time does the clock show? Write the number.

Getting Ready for Grade 1

forty-three **GR43**

GR: Practice, p. GRP19

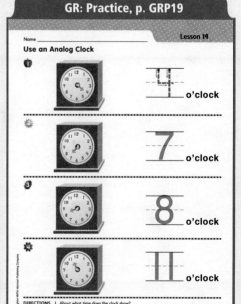

GR: Reteach, p. GRR19

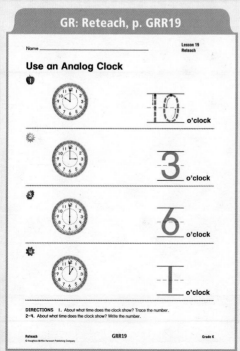

***GR** – Getting Ready Lessons and Resources (*www.thinkcentral.com*)

before 6 o'clock   about 6 o'clock   after 6 o'clock

5

before 2 o'clock

(about 2 o'clock)

after 2 o'clock

6

before 7 o'clock

about 7 o'clock

(after 7 o'clock)

7

(before 11 o'clock)

about 11 o'clock

after 11 o'clock

DIRECTIONS 5–7. Circle the time shown on the clock.

 HOME ACTIVITY • Look at or draw a simple clock. Ask your child questions such as: *Where does the hour hand go to show about 8 o'clock? About 1 o'clock? About 4 o'clock?*

© Houghton Mifflin Harcourt Publishing Company

GR44 forty-four

---

2 **PRACTICE**

Have children locate Exercise 1.

- **Where is the hour hand pointing?** toward the number 2
- **What does it mean when the hour hand is pointing toward the number 2?** It is about 2 o'clock. **Trace the number.**

Have children locate Exercise 2.

- **Which number is the hour hand pointing to?** 5
- **What does that mean?** It is about 5 o'clock. **Write the number.**
- **How are the clocks in Exercises 1 and 2 different?** They show different times.

Continue to ask questions about the hour hand on the clock for Exercises 3 and 4.

Have children look at the model watches above Exercise 5. Explain that the watch on the left shows the time as before 6 o'clock because the hour hand is pointing before the 6. The watch in the middle shows the time as about 6 o'clock because the hour hand is pointing toward the 6. The watch on the right shows the time as after 6 o'clock because the hour hand is pointing after the 6.

- **How do you know whether the time is before the hour, about the hour, or after the hour?** I look to see whether the hour hand is before, on, or after the number that shows the hour.

Read the phrases with the children for Exercises 5–7. Have children circle the time that each watch shows.

3 **SUMMARIZE**

MATHEMATICAL PRACTICES

Essential Question

How can you use a clock to tell time? I look at the hour hand to see which number it is pointing toward.

Math Journal  Math

What do you do at about 12 o'clock at school? Draw a picture. Write the number 12.

LESSON 20

Use a Digital Clock

LESSON AT A GLANCE

Common Core Standards
Know number names and the count sequence.
K.CC.A.3 Write numbers from 0 to 20. Represent a number of objects with a written numeral 0–20 (with 0 representing a count of no objects).

Tell and write time.
1.MD.B.3 Tell and write time in hours and half-hours using analog and digital clocks.

Lesson Objective
Write the hour, using a digital clock.

Essential Question
How can you write numbers to show hours, using a digital clock?

Materials
MathBoard

1 TEACH and TALK

Materials *i*Tools: Measurement

Show children the *i*Tools digital clock (or draw a digital clock on the board). Explain that a digital clock does not have hands, but it does have numbers. The numbers change as the time changes. Show the time at 12:00.

- **What number do you see to the left of the dots?** 12 **What time is shown on the clock?** 12 o'clock

Forward the clock to 1:00.

- **What number do you see to the left of the dots now?** 1 **What is the time?** 1 o'clock

Forward the clock to 2:00.

- **What number do you see to the left of the dots now?** 2 **What is the time?** 2 o'clock

Continue forwarding the clock 1 hour at a time. Have children read the numbers to the left of the dots and say the times.

This lesson builds on writing numbers to 20 presented in Chapters 7–8 and prepares children for telling and writing time taught in Grade 1.

Name _____

Use a Digital Clock

① 10:00 → 10 o'clock

② 3:00 → 3 o'clock

③ 5:00 → 5 o'clock

④ 12:00 → 12 o'clock

DIRECTIONS 1. Trace the hour number on the digital clock. Trace to show another way to write that time. 2–4. Trace the hour number on the digital clock. Show another way to write that time.

Getting Ready for Grade 1   forty-five **GR45**

GR: Practice, p. GRP20

Name _____   Lesson **20**
Use a Digital Clock

① 4:00 → 4 o'clock
② 10:00 → 10 o'clock
③ 9:00 → 9 o'clock
④ 7:00 → 7 o'clock

DIRECTIONS 1. Trace the hour number on the digital clock. Trace to show another way to write that time. 2–4. Trace the hour number on the digital clock. Show another way to write that time.

Getting Ready Practice   GRP20

GR: Reteach, p. GRR20

Name _____   Lesson 20
Reteach
Use a Digital Clock

① 2:00 → 2 o'clock
② 1:00 → 1 o'clock
③ 5:00 → 5 o'clock
④ 8:00 → 8 o'clock

DIRECTIONS Look at the hour number on the digital clock. 1. Trace to show another way to write that time. 2–4. Show another way to write that time.

Reteach   GRR20   Grade K

PG88   Planning Guide

*GR – Getting Ready Lessons and Resources (*www.thinkcentral.com*)

5 6:00 — 6 o'clock

6 2:00 — 2 o'clock

7 11:00 — 11 o'clock

8 8:00 — 8 o'clock

DIRECTIONS 5–8. Trace the hour number on the digital clock. Show another way to write that time.

HOME ACTIVITY • Ask your child to explain or draw what a digital clock looks like at 3:00.

GR46 forty-six

© Houghton Mifflin Harcourt Publishing Company

---

② PRACTICE MATH BOARD

Have children locate Exercise 1.

- **What is the number to the left of the dots on the digital clock?** 10

Have children trace 10 on the clock.

- **What is the time?** 10 o'clock

Have children trace the 10 next to "o'clock."

Have children locate the digital clock in Exercise 2.

- **What is the number to the left of the dots on the clock?** 3
- **What is the time?** 3 o'clock
- **What number will you write next to "o'clock"?** 3

Have children trace the 3 on the clock and write 3 to show the time. Continue similarly for Exercises 3–8.

③ SUMMARIZE

Common Core **MATHEMATICAL PRACTICES**

Essential Question

How can you write numbers to show hours using a digital clock? To show the hour on the clock, I write a number 1 to 10 to the left of the dots. If the number is 5, the time is 5 o'clock.

Math Journal  Math

You may want children to place these pages in a Math Journal.

Getting Ready Lessons and Resources, pp. GR47–GR48   ✓ **Checkpoint**

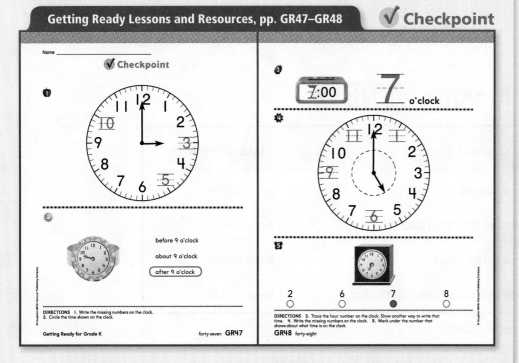

Name _____

✓ Checkpoint

1

2

before 9 o'clock

about 9 o'clock

after 9 o'clock

DIRECTIONS 1. Write the missing numbers on the clock. 2. Circle the time shown on the clock.

Getting Ready for Grade K   forty-seven **GR47**

© Houghton Mifflin Harcourt Publishing Company

3 7:00 — 7 o'clock

4

5

2   6   7   8

DIRECTIONS 3. Trace the hour number on the clock. Show another way to write that time. 4. Write the missing numbers on the clock. 5. Mark under the number that shows about what time is on the clock.

GR48 forty-eight

© Houghton Mifflin Harcourt Publishing Company

Getting Ready for Grade 1
Test

LESSONS 14 TO 20

Summative Assessment

Use the **Getting Ready Test** to assess children's progress in Getting Ready for Grade 1 Lessons 14–20.

Getting Ready Tests are provided in multiple-choice and mixed-response format in the *Getting Ready Lessons and Resources*.

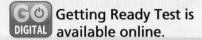 Getting Ready Test is available online.

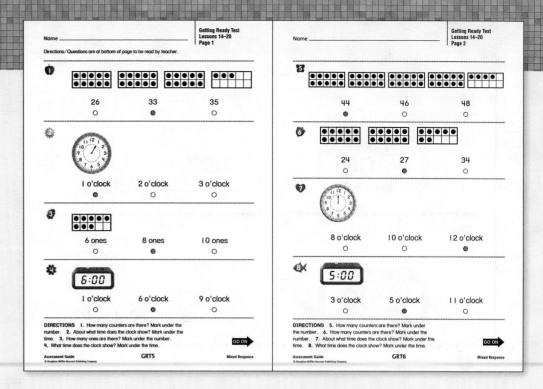

✓ Data-Driven Decision Making 🔺 RtI

Item	Lesson	Common Error	Intervene With
1, 10	16	May not understand how to count from 30 to 40	R—p. GRR16
2, 7, 15	19	May not understand what the hour hand means	R—p. GRR19
3, 9	14	May not understand how to count ones	R—p. GRR14
4, 8, 14	20	May not understand how to read hours on a digital clock	R—p. GRR20

Key: R—Getting Ready Lessons and Resources: Reteach

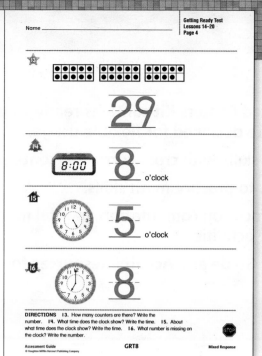

Portfolio Suggestions The portfolio represents the growth, talents, achievements, and reflections of the mathematics learner. Children might spend a short time selecting work samples for their portfolios.

You may want to have children respond to the following questions:

- Which question was difficult?
- What would you like to learn more about?

For information about how to organize, share, and evaluate portfolios, see the *Chapter Resources*.

✓ Data-Driven Decision Making  RtI

Item	Lesson	Common Error	Intervene With
5, 11	17	May not understand how to count from 40 to 50	**R**—p. GRR17
6, 13	15	May not understand how to count from 20 to 30	**R**—p. GRR15
12, 16	18	May confuse the order of numbers on an analog clock face	**R**—p. GRR18

Key: R—Getting Ready Lessons and Resources: Reteach

The Grab-and-Go!™ Differentiated Centers Kit contains ready-to-use readers, games, and math center activities that are designed for flexible usage.

- Readers that integrate math skills with cross-curricular content.
- Games that engage students to practice math skills.
- Math Center Activities that focus on computation, mental math, geometry, measurement, and challenge activities.

See the Grab-and-Go!™ Teacher Guide and Activity Resources for more information.

Chapter	Grade K		
1 Represent, Count, and Write Numbers 0 to 5	Reader	Pancakes for All The Red Caboose	
	Game	Bus Stop	
	Activity	Activity 5	Numbers 2 and 3 Numbers 1 and 2 Number 3
		Activity 6	Get It Together!
		Activity 7	Numbers 1 to 5 Now You See It Up to 5
2 Compare Numbers to 5	Reader	Mabel's Place	
	Game	Bus Stop	
	Activity	Activity 7	Numbers 1 to 5 Now You See It Up to 5
3 Represent, Count, and Write Numbers 6 to 9	Reader	Mabel's Place A Nutty Story	
	Game	Bus Stop	
	Activity	Activity 15	Sensational Seven Super Six At 6s and 7s
		Activity 17	Seeing Eight Eight and Nine Are Fine!

Chapter		Grade K	
4 Represent and Compare Numbers to 10	**Reader**	I Know Numbers Raccoons' Playtime	
	Activity	Activity 17	Roundup
5 Addition	**Reader**	Pancakes for All Flowers for Fossie	
	Game	Spin to Add	
	Activity	Activity 6	Come Together! Get It Together! All Together Now!
		Activity 15	Sensational Seven
		Activity 18	Together Again!
6 Subtraction	**Reader**	Numbers at the Lake Under the Umbrellas	
	Game	Sailboat Subtraction	
	Activity	Activity 8	Away They Go! Bye Bye! Leftovers!
		Activity 16	I'm Taken!
		Activity 18	Add and Subtract

Math Center Activity Cards:

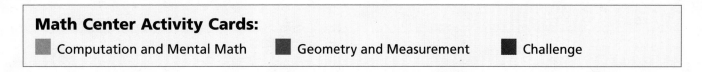

Computation and Mental Math   Geometry and Measurement   Challenge

Chapter	Grade K			
7 Represent, Count, and Write 11 to 19	**Reader**	Stop the Picnic! Summertime Math!		
	Game	Sweet and Sour Path		
	Activity	Activity 14	13 and 14 11 and 12 15 and 16	
		Activity 20	19 and 20 17 and 18	
8 Represent, Count, and Write 20 and Beyond	**Reader**	Where's the Party? Summertime Math! Counting at the Market		
	Game	Sweet and Sour Path		
	Activity	Activity 17	Roundup	
		Activity 20	19 and 20 Place Your Order	
9 Identify and Describe Two-Dimensional Shapes	**Reader**	And the Wheels Go Round I Know Shapes Hippo and Fox Sort Socks		
	Game	Follow the Figures Number Picture		
	Activity	Activity 3	Same Game	

Chapter		Grade K	
10 Identify and Describe Three-Dimensional Shapes	**Reader**	I Know Big and Small Curious George® Goes to a Toy Store Up, Up to the Top	
	Activity	Activity 9	Top of the Heap Tip Top Think Outside the Box
		Activity 12	Find the Shapes Get In Shape
11 Measurement	**Reader**	Who Am I? Shortest and Longest Where I Live Curious George® and the Mystery Boxes	
	Game	Connecting Cube Challenge	
	Activity	Activity 19	Ups and Downs! Long and Short An Order to Go!
12 Classify and Sort Data	**Reader**	Hippo and Fox Sort Socks I Know Alike and Different I Know Big and Small Shells! Shells!	
	Game	Spill the Counters	
	Activity	Activity 1	Mix and Match
		Activity 3	Think Big Color It Same Game
		Activity 10	Get a Graph Sort and Graph

Math Center Activity Cards:

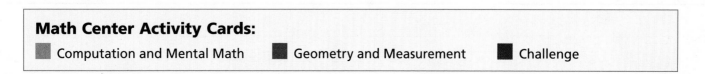

■ Computation and Mental Math   ■ Geometry and Measurement   ■ Challenge

Sequence Options

GO Math! provides the flexibility to teach the program in a different sequence. If children need background knowledge for the chapter, use the list of prerequisites.

Chapter	Objectives	Prerequisites
1 Represent, Count, and Write Numbers 0 to 5 COMMON CORE STATE STANDARDS K.CC.A.3, K.CC.B.4a, K.CC.B.4b, K.CC.B.4c, K.OA.A.3	• Model and count to tell the number of objects 0–5. • Represent objects 0–5 with a number name and a written numeral. • Solve problems by using the strategy *make a model*.	
2 Compare Numbers to 5 COMMON CORE STATE STANDARDS K.CC.C.6	• Use matching and counting strategies to compare sets to 5. • Make a model to solve problems using a matching strategy.	Chapter 1
3 Represent, Count, and Write Numbers 6 to 9 COMMON CORE STATE STANDARDS K.CC.A.3, K.CC.B.5, K.CC.C.6	• Model and count to tell the number of objects 6–9. • Represent objects 6–9 with a number name and a written numeral. • Solve problems by using the strategy *draw a picture*.	Chapters 1, 2
4 Represent and Compare Numbers to 10 COMMON CORE STATE STANDARDS K.CC.A.2, K.CC.A.3, K.CC.B.5, K.CC.C.6, K.CC.C.7, K.OA.A.4	• Model, count, and represent objects to 10 with a number name and a written numeral. • Use a drawing to make 10 from a given number. • Count forward to 10 from a given number. • Use counting strategies to compare sets of objects. • Solve problems by using the strategy *make a model*.	Chapters 1–3
5 Addition COMMON CORE STATE STANDARDS K.OA.A.1, K.OA.A.2, K.OA.A.3, K.OA.A.4, K.OA.A.5	• Use expressions to represent addition. • Use objects and drawings to solve addition word problems and record the equations. • Decompose numbers into pairs in more than one way and record each decomposition with an equation. • Solve problems by using the strategy *act it out*.	Chapters 1, 3, 4
6 Subtraction COMMON CORE STATE STANDARDS K.OA.A.1, K.OA.A.2, K.OA.A.5	• Use expressions to represent subtraction. • Use objects and drawings to solve subtraction word problems and record the equations. • Understand addition as putting together or adding to and subtraction as taking apart or taking from to solve word problems. • Solve problems by using the strategy *act it out*.	Chapters 1, 3, 4
7 Represent, Count, and Write 11 to 19 COMMON CORE STATE STANDARDS K.CC.A.3, K.NBT.A.1	• Use objects to decompose numbers 11 through 19 into ten ones and some further ones. • Represent 11 to 19 objects with number names and written numerals. • Solve problems by using the strategy *draw a picture*.	Chapters 1–4

Chapter	Objectives	Prerequisites
8 Represent, Count, and Write 20 and Beyond COMMON CORE STATE STANDARDS K.CC.A.1, K.CC.A.2, K.CC.A.3, K.CC.B.5, K.CC.C.6	• Model and count with objects to show the number 20 and beyond. • Represent 20 objects and more with a number name and a written numeral. • Count forward to 20 from a given number. • Know the count sequence when counting to 50 and to 100 by ones and by tens. • Solve problems by using the strategy *make a model*.	Chapters 1, 3, 4, 7
9 Identify and Describe Two-Dimensional Shapes COMMON CORE STATE STANDARDS K.G.A.2, K.G.B.4, K.G.B.6	• Identify, name, describe, and compare two-dimensional shapes including square, circle, triangle, rectangle, and hexagon. • Solve problems by using the strategy *draw a picture*.	Chapters 1, 3
10 Identify and Describe Three-Dimensional Shapes COMMON CORE STATE STANDARDS K.G.A.1, K.G.A.2, K.G.A.3, K.G.B.4	• Identify, name, describe, and compare three-dimensional shapes including cube, cone, cylinder, and sphere. • Analyze, compare, create, and compose shapes. • Solve problems by using the strategy *use logical reasoning*.	
11 Measurement COMMON CORE STATE STANDARDS K.MD.A.1, K.MD.A.2	• Compare the length, height, and weight of two objects. • Describe several measurable attributes of a single object. • Solve problems by using the strategy *draw a picture*.	Chapters 2, 4
12 Classify and Sort Data COMMON CORE STATE STANDARDS K.MD.B.3	• Classify objects by color, shape, and size and count the number of objects in each category. • Make and read a graph to count objects that have been classified into categories. • Solve problems by using the strategy *use logical reasoning*.	Chapters 1–5, 9

Instructional Path

Lesson	Common Core State Standards for Mathematics		Pacing
Chapter 1 Represent, Count, and Write Numbers 0 to 5			
Progress Tracker **1** 2 3 4 5 6 7 8 9 10 11 12			
1.1 Hands On • Model and Count 1 and 2	■ K.CC.B.4.a	When counting objects, say the number names in the standard order, pairing each object with one and only one number name and each number name with one and only one object.	1 day
1.2 Count and Write 1 and 2	■ K.CC.A.3	Write numbers from 0 to 20. Represent a number of objects with a written numeral 0–20 (with 0 representing a count of no objects).	2 days
1.3 Hands On • Model and Count 3 and 4	■ K.CC.B.4.a	When counting objects, say the number names in the standard order, pairing each object with one and only one number name and each number name with one and only one object.	1 day
1.4 Count and Write 3 and 4	■ K.CC.A.3	Write numbers from 0 to 20. Represent a number of objects with a written numeral 0–20 (with 0 representing a count of no objects).	2 days
1.5 Hands On • Model and Count to 5	■ K.CC.B.4.a	When counting objects, say the number names in the standard order, pairing each object with one and only one number name and each number name with one and only one object.	2 days
1.6 Count and Write to 5	■ K.CC.A.3	Write numbers from 0 to 20. Represent a number of objects with a written numeral 0–20 (with 0 representing a count of no objects).	2 days
1.7 Hands On: Algebra • Ways to Make 5	■ K.OA.A.3 ■ K.CC.B.4.b	Write numbers from 0 to 20. Represent a number of objects with a written numeral 0–20 (with 0 representing a count of no objects). Understand that the last number name said tells the number of objects counted. The number of objects is the same regardless of their arrangement or the order in which they were counted.	2 days
1.8 Hands On • Count and Order to 5	■ K.CC.B.4.c	Understand that each successive number name refers to a quantity that is one larger.	2 days
1.9 Problem Solving • Understand 0	■ K.CC.A.3	Write numbers from 0 to 20. Represent a number of objects with a written numeral 0–20 (with 0 representing a count of no objects).	2 days
1.10 Identify and Write 0	■ K.CC.A.3	Write numbers from 0 to 20. Represent a number of objects with a written numeral 0–20 (with 0 representing a count of no objects).	1 day

Lesson	Common Core State Standards for Mathematics		Pacing
Chapter 2 Compare Numbers to 5			
Progress Tracker 1 **2** 3 4 5 6 7 8 9 10 11 12			
2.1 Hands On • Same Number	■ K.CC.C.6	Identify whether the number of objects in one group is greater than, less than, or equal to the number of objects in another group, e.g., by using matching and counting strategies. (Include groups with up to ten objects.)	2 days
2.2 Hands On • Greater Than	■ K.CC.C.6	Identify whether the number of objects in one group is greater than, less than, or equal to the number of objects in another group, e.g., by using matching and counting strategies. (Include groups with up to ten objects.)	2 days

Chapter continued on next page ▶

Lesson	Common Core State Standards for Mathematics		Pacing
Chapter 2 Compare Numbers to 5 *(continued)*			
2.3 Hands On • Less Than	■ **K.CC.C.6**	Identify whether the number of objects in one group is greater than, less than, or equal to the number of objects in another group, e.g., by using matching and counting strategies. (Include groups with up to ten objects.	2 days
2.4 Problem Solving • Compare by Matching Sets to 5	■ **K.CC.C.6**	Identify whether the number of objects in one group is greater than, less than, or equal to the number of objects in another group, e.g., by using matching and counting strategies. (Include groups with up to ten objects.)	2 days
2.5 Compare by Counting Sets to 5	■ **K.CC.C.6**	Identify whether the number of objects in one group is greater than, less than, or equal to the number of objects in another group, e.g., by using matching and counting strategies. (Include groups with up to ten objects.)	2 days

Chapter 3 Represent, Count, and Write Numbers 6 to 9			

Progress Tracker   1   2   **3**   4   5   6   7   8   9   10   11   12

Lesson	Common Core State Standards for Mathematics		Pacing
3.1 Hands On • Model and Count 6	■ **K.CC.B.5**	Count to answer "how many?" questions about as many as 20 things arranged in a line, a rectangular array, or a circle, or as many as 10 things in a scattered configuration; given a number from 1–20, count out that many objects.	2 days
3.2 Count and Write to 6	■ **K.CC.A.3**	Write numbers from 0 to 20. Represent a number of objects with a written numeral 0–20 (with 0 representing a count of no objects).	1 day
3.3 Hands On • Model and Count 7	■ **K.CC.B.5**	Count to answer "how many?" questions about as many as 20 things arranged in a line, a rectangular array, or a circle, or as many as 10 things in a scattered configuration; given a number from 1–20, count out that many objects.	2 days
3.4 Count and Write to 7	■ **K.CC.A.3**	Write numbers from 0 to 20. Represent a number of objects with a written numeral 0–20 (with 0 representing a count of no objects).	1 day
3.5 Hands On • Model and Count 8	■ **K.CC.B.5**	Count to answer "how many?" questions about as many as 20 things arranged in a line, a rectangular array, or a circle, or as many as 10 things in a scattered configuration; given a number from 1–20, count out that many objects.	2 days
3.6 Count and Write to 8	■ **K.CC.A.3**	Write numbers from 0 to 20. Represent a number of objects with a written numeral 0–20 (with 0 representing a count of no objects).	1 day
3.7 Hands On • Model and Count 9	■ **K.CC.B.5**	Count to answer "how many?" questions about as many as 20 things arranged in a line, a rectangular array, or a circle, or as many as 10 things in a scattered configuration; given a number from 1–20, count out that many objects.	2 days

Chapter continued on next page ▶

■ Major Content   ☐ Supporting Content   ◯ Additional Content

Lesson	Common Core State Standards for Mathematics		Pacing
Chapter 3 Represent, Count, and Write Numbers 6 to 9 *(continued)*			
3.8 Count and Write to 9	■ **K.CC.A.3**	Write numbers from 0 to 20. Represent a number of objects with a written numeral 0–20 (with 0 representing a count of no objects).	2 days
3.9 Problem Solving • Numbers to 9	■ **K.CC.C.6**	Identify whether the number of objects in one group is greater than, less than, or equal to the number of objects in another group, e.g., by using matching and counting strategies. (Include groups with up to ten objects.)	2 days
	■ **K.CC.C.7**	Compare two numbers between 1 and 10 presented as written numerals.	

Chapter 4 Represent and Compare Numbers to 10			

Progress Tracker 1 2 3 **4** 5 6 7 8 9 10 11 12

Lesson	Standards	Description	Pacing
4.1 Hands On • Model and Count 10	■ **K.CC.B.5**	Count to answer "how many?" questions about as many as 20 things arranged in a line, a rectangular array, or a circle, or as many as 10 things in a scattered configuration; given a number from 1–20, count out that many objects.	2 days
	■ **K.OA.A.3**	Decompose numbers less than or equal to 10 into pairs in more than one way, e.g., by using objects or drawings, and record each decomposition by a drawing or equation (e.g., 5 = 2 + 3 and 5 = 4 + 1).	
4.2 Count and Write to 10	■ **K.CC.A.3**	Write numbers from 0 to 20. Represent a number of objects with a written numeral 0–20 (with 0 representing a count of no objects).	2 days
4.3 Hands On: Algebra • Ways to Make 10	■ **K.OA.A.4**	For any number from 1 to 9, find the number that makes 10 when added to the given number, e.g., by using objects or drawings, and record the answer with a drawing or equation.	2 days
4.4 Count and Order to 10	■ **K.CC.A.2**	Count forward beginning from a given number within the known sequence (instead of having to begin at 1).	1 day
4.5 Problem Solving • Compare by Matching Sets to 10	■ **K.CC.C.6**	Identify whether the number of objects in one group is greater than, less than, or equal to the number of objects in another group, e.g., by using matching and counting strategies. (Include groups with up to ten objects.)	2 days
4.6 Compare by Counting Sets to 10	■ **K.CC.C.6**	Identify whether the number of objects in one group is greater than, less than, or equal to the number of objects in another group, e.g., by using matching and counting strategies. (Include groups with up to ten objects.)	2 days
4.7 Compare Two Numbers	■ **K.CC.C.7**	Compare two numbers between 1 and 10 presented as written numerals.	2 days

Lesson	Common Core State Standards for Mathematics		Pacing

Chapter 5 Addition

Progress Tracker   1   2   3   4   **5**   6   7   8   9   10   11   12

Lesson	Standard	Description	Pacing
5.1 Addition: Add To	■ K.OA.A.1	Represent addition and subtraction with objects, fingers, mental images, drawings, sounds (e.g., claps), acting out situations, verbal explanations, expressions, or equations. (Drawings need not show details, but should show the mathematics in the problem.)	1 day
5.2 Hands On • Addition: Put Together	■ K.OA.A.1	Represent addition and subtraction with objects, fingers, mental images, drawings, sounds (e.g., claps), acting out situations, verbal explanations, expressions, or equations. (Drawings need not show details, but should show the mathematics in the problem.)	2 days
5.3 Problem Solving • Act Out Addition Problems	■ K.OA.A.1	Represent addition and subtraction with objects, fingers, mental images, drawings, sounds (e.g., claps), acting out situations, verbal explanations, expressions, or equations. (Drawings need not show details, but should show the mathematics in the problem.)	2 days
5.4 Hands On: Algebra • Model and Draw Addition Problems	■ K.OA.A.5	Fluently add and subtract within 5.	2 days
5.5 Algebra • Write Addition Sentences for 10	■ K.OA.A.4	For any number from 1 to 9, find the number that makes 10 when added to the given number, e.g., by using objects or drawings, and record the answer with a drawing or equation.	1 day
5.6 Algebra • Write Addition Sentences	■ K.OA.A.5	Fluently add and subtract within 5.	2 days
5.7 Algebra • Write More Addition Sentences	■ K.OA.A.2	Solve addition and subtraction word problems, and add and subtract within 10, e.g., by using objects or drawings to represent the problem.	2 days
5.8 Hands On: Algebra • Number Pairs to 5	■ K.OA.A.3	Decompose numbers less than or equal to 10 into pairs in more than one way, e.g., by using objects or drawings, and record each decomposition by a drawing or equation (e.g., 5 = 2 + 3 and 5 = 4 + 1).	2 days
5.9 Hands On: Algebra • Number Pairs for 6 and 7	■ K.OA.A.3	Decompose numbers less than or equal to 10 into pairs in more than one way, e.g., by using objects or drawings, and record each decomposition by a drawing or equation (e.g., 5 = 2 + 3 and 5 = 4 + 1).	1 day
5.10 Hands On: Algebra • Number Pairs for 8	■ K.OA.A.3	Decompose numbers less than or equal to 10 into pairs in more than one way, e.g., by using objects or drawings, and record each decomposition by a drawing or equation (e.g., 5 = 2 + 3 and 5 = 4 + 1).	1 day
5.11 Hands On: Algebra • Number Pairs for 9	■ K.OA.A.3	Decompose numbers less than or equal to 10 into pairs in more than one way, e.g., by using objects or drawings, and record each decomposition by a drawing or equation (e.g., 5 = 2 + 3 and 5 = 4 + 1).	1 day
5.12 Hands On: Algebra • Number Pairs for 10	■ K.OA.A.3	Decompose numbers less than or equal to 10 into pairs in more than one way, e.g., by using objects or drawings, and record each decomposition by a drawing or equation (e.g., 5 = 2 + 3 and 5 = 4 + 1).	2 days

■ Major Content   ☐ Supporting Content   ○ Additional Content

Lesson	Common Core State Standards for Mathematics		Pacing
Chapter 6 Subtraction			
Progress Tracker 1 2 3 4 5 **6** 7 8 9 10 11 12			
6.1 Subtraction: Take From	▪ K.OA.A.1	Represent addition and subtraction with objects, fingers, mental images, drawings, sounds (e.g., claps), acting out situations, verbal explanations, expressions, or equations. (Drawings need not show details, but should show the mathematics in the problem.)	1 day
6.2 Hands On • Subtraction: Take Apart	▪ K.OA.A.1	Represent addition and subtraction with objects, fingers, mental images, drawings, sounds (e.g., claps), acting out situations, verbal explanations, expressions, or equations. (Drawings need not show details, but should show the mathematics in the problem.)	2 days
6.3 Problem Solving • Act Out Subtraction Problems	▪ K.OA.A.1	Represent addition and subtraction with objects, fingers, mental images, drawings, sounds (e.g., claps), acting out situations, verbal explanations, expressions, or equations. (Drawings need not show details, but should show the mathematics in the problem.)	2 days
6.4 Hands On: Algebra • Model and Draw Subtraction Problems	▪ K.OA.A.5	Fluently add and subtract within 5.	2 days
6.5 Algebra • Write Subtraction Sentences	▪ K.OA.A.5	Fluently add and subtract within 5.	2 days
6.6 Algebra • Write More Subtraction Sentences	▪ K.OA.A.2	Solve addition and subtraction word problems, and add and subtract within 10, e.g., by using objects or drawings to represent the problem.	2 days
6.7 Hands On: Algebra • Addition and Subtraction	▪ K.OA.A.2	Solve addition and subtraction word problems, and add and subtract within 10, e.g., by using objects or drawings to represent the problem.	2 days

Lesson	Common Core State Standards for Mathematics		Pacing
Chapter 7 Represent, Count, and Write Numbers 11 to 19			
Progress Tracker 1 2 3 4 5 6 **7** 8 9 10 11 12			
7.1 Hands On • Model and Count 11 and 12	▪ K.NBT.A.1	Compose and decompose numbers from 11 to 19 into ten ones and some further ones, e.g., by using objects or drawings, and record each composition or decomposition by a drawing or equation (e.g., $18 = 10 + 8$); understand that these numbers are composed of ten ones and one, two, three, four, five, six, seven, eight, or nine ones.	2 days
7.2 Count and Write 11 and 12	▪ K.NBT.A.1	Compose and decompose numbers from 11 to 19 into ten ones and some further ones, e.g., by using objects or drawings, and record each composition or decomposition by a drawing or equation (e.g., $18 = 10 + 8$); understand that these numbers are composed of ten ones and one, two, three, four, five, six, seven, eight, or nine ones.	1 day

Chapter continued on next page ▶

Lesson	Common Core State Standards for Mathematics		Pacing
Chapter 7 Represent, Count, and Write Numbers 11 to 19 *(continued)*			
7.3 Hands On • Model and Count 13 and 14	■ K.NBT.A.1	Compose and decompose numbers from 11 to 19 into ten ones and some further ones, e.g., by using objects or drawings, and record each composition or decomposition by a drawing or equation (e.g., 18 = 10 + 8); understand that these numbers are composed of ten ones and one, two, three, four, five, six, seven, eight, or nine ones.	2 days
7.4 Count and Write 13 and 14	■ K.NBT.A.1	Compose and decompose numbers from 11 to 19 into ten ones and some further ones, e.g., by using objects or drawings, and record each composition or decomposition by a drawing or equation (e.g., 18 = 10 + 8); understand that these numbers are composed of ten ones and one, two, three, four, five, six, seven, eight, or nine ones.	1 day
7.5 Hands On • Model, Count, and Write 15	■ K.NBT.A.1	Compose and decompose numbers from 11 to 19 into ten ones and some further ones, e.g., by using objects or drawings, and record each composition or decomposition by a drawing or equation (e.g., 18 = 10 + 8); understand that these numbers are composed of ten ones and one, two, three, four, five, six, seven, eight, or nine ones.	2 days
7.6 Problem Solving • Use Numbers to 15	■ K.CC.A.3	Write numbers from 0 to 20. Represent a number of objects with a written numeral 0–20 (with 0 representing a count of no objects).	2 days
7.7 Hands On • Model and Count 16 and 17	■ K.NBT.A.1	Compose and decompose numbers from 11 to 19 into ten ones and some further ones, e.g., by using objects or drawings, and record each composition or decomposition by a drawing or equation (e.g., 18 = 10 + 8); understand that these numbers are composed of ten ones and one, two, three, four, five, six, seven, eight, or nine ones.	2 days
7.8 Count and Write 16 and 17	■ K.NBT.A.1	Compose and decompose numbers from 11 to 19 into ten ones and some further ones, e.g., by using objects or drawings, and record each composition or decomposition by a drawing or equation (e.g., 18 = 10 + 8); understand that these numbers are composed of ten ones and one, two, three, four, five, six, seven, eight, or nine ones.	1 day
7.9 Hands On • Model and Count 18 and 19	■ K.NBT.A.1	Compose and decompose numbers from 11 to 19 into ten ones and some further ones, e.g., by using objects or drawings, and record each composition or decomposition by a drawing or equation (e.g., 18 = 10 + 8); understand that these numbers are composed of ten ones and one, two, three, four, five, six, seven, eight, or nine ones.	2 days
7.10 Count and Write 18 and 19	■ K.NBT.A.1	Compose and decompose numbers from 11 to 19 into ten ones and some further ones, e.g., by using objects or drawings, and record each composition or decomposition by a drawing or equation (e.g., 18 = 10 + 8); understand that these numbers are composed of ten ones and one, two, three, four, five, six, seven, eight, or nine ones.	2 days

■ Major Content   ☐ Supporting Content   ○ Additional Content

Lesson	Common Core State Standards for Mathematics	Pacing

Chapter 8 Represent, Count, and Write 20 and Beyond

Progress Tracker 1 2 3 4 5 6 7 **8** 9 10 11 12

Lesson	Standard	Description	Pacing
8.1 Hands On • Model and Count 20	■ K.CC.B.5	Count to answer "how many?" questions about as many as 20 things arranged in a line, a rectangular array, or a circle, or as many as 10 things in a scattered configuration; given a number from 1–20, count out that many objects.	2 days
8.2 Count and Write to 20	■ K.CC.A.3	Write numbers from 0 to 20. Represent a number of objects with a written numeral 0–20 (with 0 representing a count of no objects).	2 days
8.3 Count and Order to 20	■ K.CC.A.2	Count forward beginning from a given number within the known sequence (instead of having to begin at 1).	2 days
8.4 Problem Solving • Compare Numbers to 20	■ K.CC.C.6	Identify whether the number of objects in one group is greater than, less than, or equal to the number of objects in another group, e.g., by using matching and counting strategies. (Include groups with up to ten objects.)	2 days
8.5 Count to 50 by Ones	■ K.CC.A.1	Count to 100 by ones and by tens.	1 day
	■ K.CC.A.2	Count forward beginning from a given number within the known sequence (instead of having to begin at 1).	
8.6 Count to 100 by Ones	■ K.CC.A.1	Count to 100 by ones and by tens.	2 days
	■ K.CC.C.7	Compare two numbers between 1 and 10 presented as written numerals.	
8.7 Count to 100 by Tens	■ K.CC.A.1	Count to 100 by ones and by tens.	2 days
8.8 Count by Tens	■ K.CC.A.1	Count to 100 by ones and by tens.	2 days

Chapter 9 Identify and Describe Two-Dimensional Shapes

Progress Tracker 1 2 3 4 5 6 7 8 **9** 10 11 12

Lesson	Standard	Description	Pacing
9.1 Identify and Name Circles	○ K.G.A.2	Correctly name shapes regardless of their orientations or overall size.	1 day
9.2 Describe Circles	□ K.G.B.4	Analyze and compare two- and three-dimensional shapes, in different sizes and orientations, using informal language to describe their similarities, differences, parts (e.g., number of sides and vertices/ "corners") and other attributes (e.g., having sides of equal length).	
9.3 Identify and Name Squares	○ K.G.A.2	Correctly name shapes regardless of their orientations or overall size.	1 day
9.4 Describe Squares	□ K.G.B.4	Analyze and compare two- and three-dimensional shapes, in different sizes and orientations, using informal language to describe their similarities, differences, parts (e.g., number of sides and vertices/ "corners") and other attributes (e.g., having sides of equal length).	

Chapter continued on next page ▶

Lesson	Common Core State Standards for Mathematics		Pacing
Chapter 9 Identify and Describe Two-Dimensional Shapes *(continued)*			
9.5 Identify and Name Triangles	○ **K.G.A.2**	Correctly name shapes regardless of their orientations or overall size.	1 day
9.6 Describe Triangles	☐ **K.G.B.4**	Analyze and compare two- and three-dimensional shapes, in different sizes and orientations, using informal language to describe their similarities, differences, parts (e.g., number of sides and vertices/"corners") and other attributes (e.g., having sides of equal length).	
9.7 Identify and Name Rectangles	○ **K.G.A.2**	Correctly name shapes regardless of their orientations or overall size.	1 day
9.8 Describe Rectangles	☐ **K.G.B.4**	Analyze and compare two- and three-dimensional shapes, in different sizes and orientations, using informal language to describe their similarities, differences, parts (e.g., number of sides and vertices/"corners") and other attributes (e.g., having sides of equal length).	
9.9 Identify and Name Hexagons	○ **K.G.A.2**	Correctly name shapes regardless of their orientations or overall size.	1 day
9.10 Describe Hexagons	☐ **K.G.B.4**	Analyze and compare two- and three-dimensional shapes, in different sizes and orientations, using informal language to describe their similarities, differences, parts (e.g., number of sides and vertices/"corners") and other attributes (e.g., having sides of equal length).	
9.11 Hands On: Algebra • Compare Two-Dimensional Shapes	☐ **K.G.B.4**	Analyze and compare two- and three-dimensional shapes, in different sizes and orientations, using informal language to describe their similarities, differences, parts (e.g., number of sides and vertices/"corners") and other attributes (e.g., having sides of equal length).	1 day
9.12 Problem Solving • Draw to Join Shapes	☐ **K.G.B.6**	Compose simple shapes to form larger shapes. *For example, "Can you join these two triangles with full sides touching to make a rectangle?"*	1 day

Chapter 10 Identify and Describe Three-Dimensional Shapes			

Progress Tracker   1   2   3   4   5   6   7   8   9   **10**   11   12

Lesson	Common Core State Standards for Mathematics		Pacing
10.1 Hands On • Three-Dimensional Shapes	☐ **K.G.B.4**	Analyze and compare two- and three-dimensional shapes, in different sizes and orientations, using informal language to describe their similarities, differences, parts (e.g., number of sides and vertices/"corners") and other attributes (e.g., having sides of equal length).	1 day
10.2 Hands On • Identify, Name, and Describe Spheres	○ **K.G.A.2**	Correctly name shapes regardless of their orientations or overall size.	1 day
10.3 Hands On • Identify, Name, and Describe Cubes	○ **K.G.A.2**	Correctly name shapes regardless of their orientations or overall size.	

■ Major Content   ☐ Supporting Content   ○ Additional Content

Chapter continued on next page ▶

Lesson	Common Core State Standards for Mathematics		Pacing
Chapter 10 Identify and Describe Three-Dimensional Shapes *(continued)*			
10.4 Hands On • Identify, Name, and Describe Cylinders	○ **K.G.A.2**	Correctly name shapes regardless of their orientations or overall size.	1 day
10.5 Hands On • Identify, Name, and Describe Cones	○ **K.G.A.2**	Correctly name shapes regardless of their orientations or overall size.	
10.6 Problem Solving • Two- and Three-Dimensional Shapes	○ **K.G.A.3**	Identify shapes as two-dimensional (lying in a plane, "flat") or three-dimensional ("solid").	1 day
10.7 Hands On • Model Shapes	☐ **K.G.B.5**	Model shapes in the world by building shapes from components (e.g., sticks and clay balls) and drawing shapes.	1 day
10.8 Above and Below	○ **K.G.A.1**	Describe objects in the environment using names of shapes, and describe the relative positions of these objects using terms such as *above, below, beside, in front of, behind,* and *next to.*	1 day
10.9 Beside and Next To	○ **K.G.A.1**	Describe objects in the environment using names of shapes, and describe the relative positions of these objects using terms such *as above, below, beside, in front of, behind,* and *next to.*	1 day
10.10 In Front Of and Behind	○ **K.G.A.1**	Describe objects in the environment using names of shapes, and describe the relative positions of these objects using terms such as *above, below, beside, in front of, behind,* and *next to.*	1 day

Chapter 11 Measurement			

Progress Tracker   1   2   3   4   5   6   7   8   9   10   **11**   12

Lesson			Pacing
11.1 Hands On • Compare Lengths	○ **K.MD.A.2**	Directly compare two objects with a measurable attribute in common, to see which object has "more of"/"less of" the attribute, and describe the difference.	1 day
11.2 Hands On • Compare Heights	○ **K.MD.A.2**	Directly compare two objects with a measurable attribute in common, to see which object has "more of"/"less of" the attribute, and describe the difference.	1 day
11.3 Problem Solving • Direct Comparison	○ **K.MD.A.2**	Directly compare two objects with a measurable attribute in common, to see which object has "more of"/"less of" the attribute, and describe the difference.	
11.4 Hands On • Compare Weights	○ **K.MD.A.2**	Directly compare two objects with a measurable attribute in common, to see which object has "more of"/"less of" the attribute, and describe the difference.	1 day
11.5 Length, Height, and Weight	○ **K.MD.A.1**	Describe measurable attributes of objects, such as length or weight. Describe several measurable attributes of a single object.	1 day

Chapter 12 Classify and Sort Data

Progress Tracker	1	2	3	4	5	6	7	8	9	10	11	12

12.1 Hands On: Algebra • Classify and Count by Color	☐ **K.MD.B.3**	Classify objects into given categories; count the numbers of objects in each category and sort the categories by count. (Limit category counts to be less than or equal to 10).	1 day
12.2 Hands On: Algebra • Classify and Count by Shape	☐ **K.MD.B.3**	Classify objects into given categories; count the numbers of objects in each category and sort the categories by count. (Limit category counts to be less than or equal to 10).	
12.3 Hands On: Algebra • Classify and Count by Size	☐ **K.MD.B.3**	Classify objects into given categories; count the numbers of objects in each category and sort the categories by count. (Limit category counts to be less than or equal to 10).	1 day
12.4 Hands On • Make a Concrete Graph	☐ **K.MD.B.3**	Classify objects into given categories; count the numbers of objects in each category and sort the categories by count. (Limit category counts to be less than or equal to 10).	1 day
12.5 Problem Solving • Read a Graph	☐ **K.MD.B.3**	Classify objects into given categories; count the numbers of objects in each category and sort the categories by count. (Limit category counts to be less than or equal to 10).	1 day

■ Major Content   ☐ Supporting Content   ○ Additional Content

Path to Fluency: Kindergarten through Grade 6

GO Math! includes a plan for helping students achieve fluency with the Common Core State Standards that are suggested for each grade. This plan provides targeted instruction and practice in the Student Edition, Teacher Edition, Teacher Resource Book, Strategies and Practice for Skills and Facts Fluency, Personal Math Trainer, and Animated Math Models. Individual components will aid students in building proficiency. Together, they offer a unique suite of materials to help all students achieve mastery.

Fluency and Memorization for Basic Facts

Grade	Standards	Resources
Kindergarten Fluency	**K.OA.A.5** Fluently add and subtract within 5.	• Games (Student Edition) • Fluency Standard Lessons (Student Edition) • Fluency Builder (Teacher Edition) • Strategies and Practice for Skills and Facts Fluency—Primary, GK–3 • Teacher Resource Book • HMH Mega Math • Personal Math Trainer: Standards Quizzes • Animated Math Models
Grade 1 Fluency	**1.OA.C.6** Add and subtract within 20, demonstrating fluency for addition and subtraction within 10. Use strategies such as counting on; making ten; decomposing a number leading to a ten; using the relationship between addition and subtraction; and creating equivalent but easier or known sums.	• Games (Student Edition) • Fluency Standard Lessons (Student Edition) • Fluency Builder (Teacher Edition) • Strategies and Practice for Skills and Facts Fluency—Primary, GK–3 • Teacher Resource Book • HMH Mega Math • Personal Math Trainer: Standards Quizzes • Animated Math Models
Grade 2 Memorization	**2.OA.B.2** Fluently add and subtract within 20 using mental strategies.	• Games (Student Edition) • Fluency Standard Lessons (Student Edition) • Fluency Builder (Teacher Edition) • Strategies and Practice for Skills and Facts Fluency—Primary, GK–3 • Teacher Resource Book • HMH Mega Math • Personal Math Trainer: Standards Quizzes • Animated Math Models
Grade 3 Memorization	**3.OA.C.7** Fluently multiply and divide within 100, using strategies such as the relationship between multiplication and division or properties of operations. By the end of Grade 3, know from memory all products of two one-digit numbers.	• Fluency Standard Lessons (Student Edition) • Fluency Builder (Teacher Edition) • Strategies and Practice for Skills and Facts Fluency—Primary, GK–3 • Strategies and Practice for Skills and Facts Fluency—Intermediate, G3–6 • Teacher Resource Book • HMH Mega Math • Personal Math Trainer: Standards Quizzes • Animated Math Models
Grades 3, 4, 5, and 6 Intervention	For those students who still need additional time for memorizing basic facts.	• Fluency Builder (Teacher Edition) • Strategies and Practice for Skills and Facts Fluency—Intermediate, G3–6 • Teacher Resource Book • HMH Mega Math • Personal Math Trainer: Standards Quizzes • Animated Math Models

Fluency for Operations with Multi-digit Numbers

Grade	Standards	Resources
Grade 2 Fluency	**2.NBT.B.5** Fluently add and subtract within 100 using strategies based on place value, properties of operations, and/or the relationship between addition and subtraction.	• Games (Student Edition) • Fluency Standard Lessons (Student Edition) • Fluency Builder (Teacher Edition) • HMH Mega Math • Personal Math Trainer: Standards Quizzes • Animated Math Models
Grade 3 Fluency	**3.NBT.A.2** Fluently add and subtract within 1000 using strategies and algorithms based on place value, properties of operations, and/or the relationship between addition and subtraction.	• Fluency Standard Lessons (Student Edition) • Fluency Builder (Teacher Edition) • Strategies and Practice for Skills and Facts Fluency—Intermediate, G3–6 • HMH Mega Math • Personal Math Trainer: Standards Quizzes • Animated Math Models
Grade 4 Fluency	**4.NBT.B.4** Fluently add and subtract multi-digit whole numbers using the standard algorithm.	• Fluency Standard Lessons (Student Edition) • Fluency Builder (Teacher Edition) • Strategies and Practice for Skills and Facts Fluency—Intermediate, G3–6 • HMH Mega Math • Personal Math Trainer: Standards Quizzes • Animated Math Models
Grade 5 Fluency	**5.NBT.B.5** Fluently multiply multi-digit whole numbers using the standard algorithm.	• Fluency Standard Lessons (Student Edition) • Fluency Builder (Teacher Edition) • Strategies and Practice for Skills and Facts Fluency—Intermediate, G3–6 • HMH Mega Math • Personal Math Trainer: Standards Quizzes • Animated Math Models
Grade 6 Fluency	**6.NS.B.2** Fluently divide multi-digit numbers using the standard algorithm. **6.NS.B.3** Fluently add, subtract, multiply, and divide multi-digit decimals using the standard algorithm for each operation.	• Fluency Standard Lessons (Student Edition) • Fluency Builder (Teacher Edition) • Strategies and Practice for Skills and Facts Fluency—Intermediate, G3–6 • Fluency Builders (Teacher Resource Book) • HMH Mega Math Personal Math Trainer: Standards Quizzes • Animated Math Models

COMMON CORE STATE STANDARDS FOR MATHEMATICS
Correlations

Standards for Mathematical Practices		Teacher Edition and Student Edition Pages
MP1	Make sense of problems and persevere in solving them.	In most Teacher Edition lessons. Some examples are: *62, 99, 167, 243, 323, 449, 661* In most Student Edition lessons. Some examples are: 61, 99, 167, 205, 243, 261, 267, 323, 341, 391
MP2	Reason abstractly and quantitatively.	In most Teacher Edition lessons. Some examples are: *67, 102, 208, 240, 286, 324–325, 524, 586, 695* In most Student Edition lessons. Some examples are: 67, 244, 249, 273, 286, 338, 393, 512, 548, 592, 689
MP3	Construct viable arguments and critique the reasoning of others.	In most Teacher Edition lessons. Some examples are: *20, 44, 99, 167, 214, 246, 326, 514, 622, 661* In most Student Edition lessons. Some examples are: 28, 81, 87, 93, 167, 361, 409, 609, 658
MP4	Model with mathematics.	In most Teacher Edition lessons. Some examples are: *64, 99, 102, 205–206, 270, 326, 391, 448, 624* In most Student Edition lessons. Some examples are: 49, 99, 119, 193, 249, 329, 391, 447, 603, 711
MP5	Use appropriate tools strategically.	In most Teacher Edition lessons. Some examples are: *56, 81, 133, 208, 318, 385, 429, 517, 585, 612* In most Student Edition lessons. Some examples are: 81, 133, 156, 181, 206, 237, 347, 429, 465, 559, 579
MP6	Attend to precision.	In most Teacher Edition lessons. Some examples are: *16, 84, 170, 214, 264, 326, 406, 466, 621, 670* In most Student Edition lessons. Some examples are: 105, 217, 240, 246, 326, 338, 532, 576, 652
MP7	Look for and make use of structure.	In most Teacher Edition lessons. Some examples are: *52, 194, 256–257, 282, 350, 465, 505, 605, 696* In most Student Edition lessons. Some examples are: 50, 157, 193, 256–257, 273, 298–299, 554–555, 603
MP8	Look for and express regularity in repeated reasoning.	In most Teacher Edition lessons. Some examples are: *58, 90, 155, 206, 217, 256, 348, 379, 461* In most Student Edition lessons. Some examples are: 44, 88, 94, 206, 298–299, 347, 465, 711

Domain: Counting and Cardinality

Teacher Edition and Student Edition Pages

■ **Cluster A: Know number names and the count sequence.**

K.CC.A.1	Count to 100 by ones and by tens.	*453A–453B*, 453–456, *459A–459B*, 459–462, *465A–465B*, 465–468, *471A–471B*, 471–474
K.CC.A.2	Count forward beginning from a given number within the known sequence (instead of having to begin at 1).	*199A–199B*, 199–201, *441A–441B*, 441–444, *453A–453B*, 453–456 See Also: *459A–459B*, 459–462
K.CC.A.3	Write numbers from 0 to 20. Represent a number of objects with a written numeral 0–20 (with 0 representing a count of no objects).	*19A–19B*, 19–22, *31A–31B*, 31–34, *43A–43B*, 43–46, *61A–61B*, 61–64, *67A–67B*, 67–70, *125A–125B*, 125–128, *137A–137B*, 137–140, *149A–149B*, 149–152, *161A–161B*, 161–164, *187A–187B*, 187–190, *435A–435B*, 435–438 See Also: *367A–367B*, 367–370, *379A–379B*, 379–382, *385A–385B*, 385–388, *403A–403B*, 403–406, *415A–415B*, 415–418

Pages only in Teacher Edition are shown in italics.

Domain continued on next page ►

■ **Cluster B: Count to tell the number of objects.**

K.CC.B.4	Understand the relationship between numbers and quantities; connect counting to cardinality.

a. When counting objects, say the number names in the standard order, pairing each object with one and only one number name and each number name with one and only one object.

13A–13B, **13–16,** *25A–25B,* **25–28,** *37A–37B,* **37–40**
See Also: *55A–55B,* 55–58, *119A–119B,* 119–122, *131A–131B,* 131–134, *143A–143B,* 143–146, *155A–155B,* 155–158, *181A–181B,* 181–184, *429A–429B,* 429–432

b. Understand that the last number name said tells the number of objects counted. The number of objects is the same regardless of their arrangement or the order in which they were counted.

49A–49B, **49–52**
See Also: *13A–13B,* 13–16, *19A–19B,* 19–22, *25A–25B,* 25–28, *31A–31B,* 31–33, *37A–37B,* 37–40, *43A–43B,* 43–46, *81A–81B,* 81–84, *119A–119B,* 119–122, *125A–125B,* 125–128, *131A–131B,* 131–134, *137A–137B,* 137–139, *143A–143B,* 143–146, *149A–149B,* 149–152, *155A–155B,* 155–158, *161A–161B,* 161–164, *181A–181B,* 181–184, *187A–187B,* 187–190, *361A–361B,* 361–364, *367A–367B,* 367–370, *373A–373B,* 373–376, *379A–379B,* 379–382, *385A–385B,* 385–388, *397A–397B,* 397–400, *403A–403B,* 403–406, *409A–409B,* 409–412, *415A–415B,* 415–418, *429A–429B,* 429–432, *435A–435B,* 435–438

c. Understand that each successive number name refers to a quantity that is one larger.

55A–55B, **55–58**
See Also: *13A–13B,* 13–16, *25A–25B,* 25–28, *31A–31B,* 31–33, *131A–131B,* 131–134, *143A–143B,* 143–146, *155A–155B,* 155–158, *181A–181B,* 181–184, *361A–361B,* 361–364, *373A–373B,* 373–376, *397A–397B,* 397–400, *409A–409B,* 409–412, *429A–429B,* 429–432

Pages only in Teacher Edition are shown in italics.

Domain continued on next page ▶

Domain: Counting and Cardinality *(continued)*	Teacher Edition and Student Edition Pages
K.CC.B.5	Count to answer "how many?" questions about as many as 20 things arranged in a line, a rectangular array, or a circle, or as many as 10 things in a scattered configuration; given a number from 1–20, count out that many objects.	*119A–119B*, 119–122, *131A–131B*, 131–134, *143A–143B*, 143–146, *155A–155B*, 155–158, *181A–181B*, 181–184, *429A–429B*, 429–432 See Also: *13A–13B*, 13–16, *19A–19B*, 19–22, *25A–25B*, 25–28, *31A–31B*, 31–33, *37A–37B*, 37–40, *43A–43B*, 43–46, *55A–55B*, 55–58, *125A–25B*, 125–128, *137A–137B*, 137–139, *149A–149B*, 149–152, *161A–161B*, 161–164, *187A–187B*, 187–190, *211A–211B*, 211–214, *361A–361B*, 361–364, *373A–373B*, 373–376, *385A–385B*, 385–388, *397A–397B*, 397–400, *409A–409B*, 409–412, *435A–435B*, 435–438

Cluster C: **Compare numbers.**

K.CC.C.6	Identify whether the number of objects in one group is greater than, less than, or equal to the number of objects in another group, e.g., by using matching and counting strategies.	*81A–81B*, 81–84, *87A–87B*, 87–90, *93A–93B*, 93–95, *99A–99B*, 99–102, *105A–105B*, 105–108, *167A–167B*, 167–170, *205A–205B*, 205–208, *211A–211B*, 211–214, *447A–447B*, 447–449 See Also: *705A–705B*, 705–708, *711A–711B*, 711–714
K.CC.C.7	Compare two numbers between 1 and 10 presented as written numerals.	*167A–167B*, 167–170, *217A–217B*, 217–220, *459A–459B*, 459–462 See Also: *81A–81B*, 81–84, *87A–87B*, 87–90, *93A–93B*, 93–95, *99A–99B*, 99–102, *105A–105B*, 105–108, *205A–205B*, 205–208, *211A–211B*, 211–214, *447A–447B*, 447–449

Domain: Operations and Algebraic Thinking	Teacher Edition and Student Edition Pages

Cluster A: **Understand addition, and understand subtraction.**

K.OA.A.1	Represent addition and subtraction with objects, fingers, mental images, drawings, sounds (e.g., claps), acting out situations, verbal explanations, expressions, or equations.	*231A–231B*, 231–234, *237A–237B*, 237–240, *243A–243B*, 243–246, *311A–311B*, 311–314, *317A–317B*, 317–320, *323A–323B*, 323–326 See Also: *249A–249B*, 249–251, *255A–255B*, 255–258, *261A–261B*, 261–264, *267A–267B*, 267–270, *329A–329B*, 329–331, *335A–335B*, 335–338, *341A–341B*, 341–344, *347A–347B*, 347–350
K.OA.A.2	Solve addition and subtraction word problems, and add and subtract within 10, e.g., by using objects or drawings to represent the problem.	*267A–267B*, 267–270, *341A–341B*, 341–344, *347A–347B*, 347–350 See Also: *249A–249B*, 249–251, *255A–255B*, 255–258, *261A–261B*, 261–264, *323A–323B*, 323–326, *329A–329B*, 329–331, *335A–335B*, 335–338

Pages only in Teacher Edition are shown in italics.

Domain continued on next page ▶

Domain: Operations and Algebraic Thinking *(continued)*

■ Cluster A: Understand addition, and understand subtraction.

K.OA.A.3	Decompose numbers less than or equal to 10 into pairs in more than one way, e.g., by using objects or drawings, and record each decomposition by a drawing or equation (e.g., 5 = 2 + 3 and 5 = 4 + 1).	*49A–49B*, 49–52, *181A–181B*, 181–184, *273A–273B*, 273–276, *279A–279B*, 279–282, *285A–285B*, 285–288, *291A–291B*, 291–294, *297A–297B*, 297–300 See Also: *193A–193B*, 193–196
K.OA.A.4	For any number from 1 to 9, find the number that makes 10 when added to the given number, e.g., by using objects or drawings, and record the answer with a drawing or equation.	*193A–193B*, 193–196, *255A–255B*, 255–258
K.OA.A.5	Fluently add and subtract within 5.	*249A–249B*, 249–251, *261A–261B*, 261–264, *329A–329B*, 329–331, *335A–335B*, 335–338 See Also: *323A–323B*, 323–326

Domain: Number and Operations in Base Ten

■ Cluster A: Work with numbers 11–19 to gain foundations for place value.

K.NBT.A.1	Compose and decompose numbers from 11 to 19 into ten ones and some further ones, e.g., by using objects or drawings, and record each composition or decomposition by a drawing or equation (such as 18 = 10 + 8); understand that these numbers are composed of ten ones and one, two, three, four, five, six, seven, eight, or nine ones.	*361A–361B*, 361–364, *367A–367B*, 367–370, *373A–373B*, 373–376, *379A–379B*, 379–382, *385A–385B*, 385–388, *397A–397B*, 397–400, *403A–403B*, 403–406, *409A–409B*, 409–412, *415A–415B*, 415–418

Domain: Measurement and Data

○ Cluster A: Describe and compare measurable attributes.

K.MD.A.1	Describe measurable attributes of objects, such as length or weight. Describe several measurable attributes of a single object.	*673A–673B*, 673–676
K.MD.A.2	Directly compare two objects with a measurable attribute in common, to see which object has "more of" / "less of" the attribute, and describe the difference.	*649A–649B*, 649–652, *655A–655B*, 655–658, *661A–661B*, 661–663, *667A–667B*, 667–670

☐ Cluster B: Classify objects and count the number of objects in each category.

K.MD.B.3	Classify objects into given categories; count the numbers of objects in each category and sort the categories by count.	*687A–687B*, 687–690, *693A–693B*, 693–696, *699A–699B*, 699–701, *705A–705B*, 705–708, *711A–711B*, 711–714

Pages only in Teacher Edition are shown in italics.

Domain: Geometry

Teacher Edition and Student Edition Pages

○ Cluster A: **Identify and describe shapes.**

K.G.A.1	Describe objects in the environment using names of shapes, and describe the relative positions of these objects using terms such as *above, below, beside, in front of, behind,* and *next to.*	*615A–615B,* 615–618, *621A–621B,* 621–624, *627A–627B,* 627–630
K.G.A.2	Correctly name shapes regardless of their orientations or overall size.	*493A–493B,* 493–496, *505A–505B,* 505–508, *517A–517B,* 517–520, *529A–529B,* 529–532, *541A–541B,* 541–544, *579A–579B,* 579–582, *585A–585B,* 585–588, *591A–591B,* 591–594, *597A–597B,* 597–599
K.G.A.3	Identify shapes as two-dimensional (lying in a plane, "flat") or three-dimensional ("solid").	*603A–603B,* 603–606

☐ Cluster B: **Analyze, compare, create, and compose shapes.**

K.G.B.4	Analyze and compare two- and three-dimensional shapes, in different sizes and orientations, using informal language to describe their similarities, differences, parts (e.g., number of sides and vertices/"corners") and other attributes (e.g., having sides of equal length).	*499A–499B,* 499–502, *511A–511B,* 511–514, *523A–523B,* 523–525, *535A–535B,* 535–538, *547A–547B,* 547–550, *553A–553B,* 553–556, *573A–573B,* 573–576
K.G.B.5	Model shapes in the world by building shapes from components (e.g., sticks and clay balls) and drawing shapes.	*609A–609B,* 609–612
K.G.B.6	Compose simple shapes to form larger shapes.	*559A–559B,* 559–562

Pages only in Teacher Edition are shown in italics.

Student Edition Glossary

H1

Picture Glossary

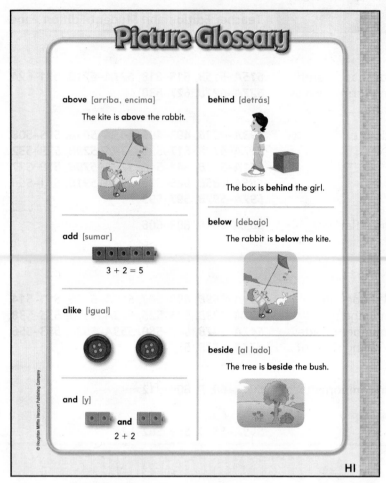

above [arriba, encima]

The kite is **above** the rabbit.

add [sumar]

$3 + 2 = 5$

alike [igual]

and [y]

and

$2 + 2$

behind [detrás]

The box is **behind** the girl.

below [debajo]

The rabbit is **below** the kite.

beside [al lado]

The tree is **beside** the bush.

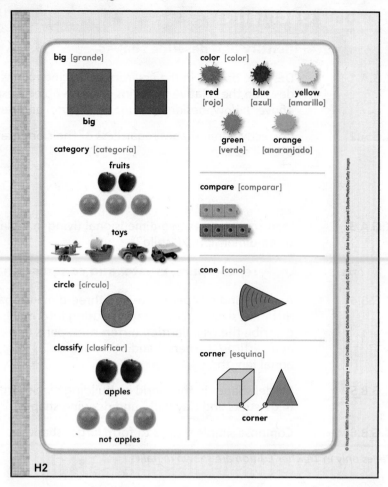

big [grande]

big

category [categoría]

fruits

toys

circle [círculo]

classify [clasificar]

apples

not apples

color [color]

red
[rojo]

blue
[azul]

yellow
[amarillo]

green
[verde]

orange
[anaranjado]

compare [comparar]

cone [cono]

corner [esquina]

corner

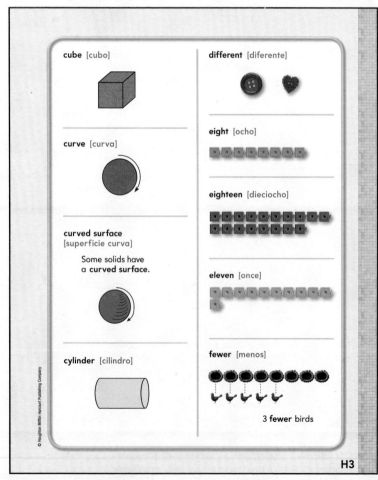

cube [cubo]

curve [curva]

curved surface
[superficie curva]

Some solids have
a **curved surface**.

cylinder [cilindro]

different [diferente]

eight [ocho]

eighteen [dieciocho]

eleven [once]

fewer [menos]

3 **fewer** birds

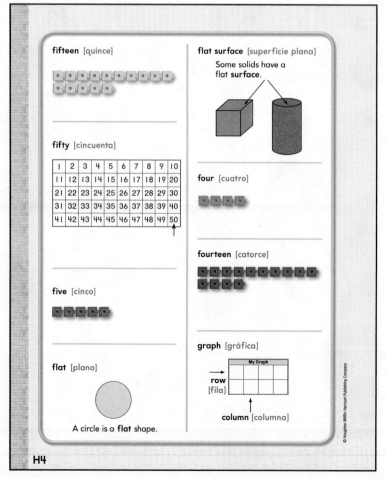

fifteen [quince]

fifty [cincuenta]

1	2	3	4	5	6	7	8	9	10
11	12	13	14	15	16	17	18	19	20
21	22	23	24	25	26	27	28	29	30
31	32	33	34	35	36	37	38	39	40
41	42	43	44	45	46	47	48	49	50

five [cinco]

flat [plano]

A circle is a **flat** shape.

flat surface [superficie plana]

Some solids have a
flat **surface**.

four [cuatro]

fourteen [catorce]

graph [gráfica]

My Graph

row
[fila]

column [columna]

H2

H3

H4

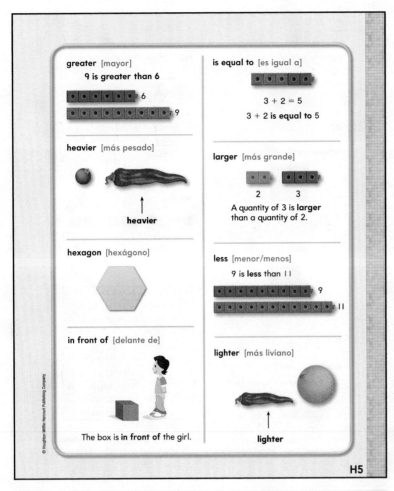

greater [mayor]

9 is greater than 6

6

9

heavier [más pesado]

heavier

hexagon [hexágono]

in front of [delante de]

The box is **in front of** the girl.

is equal to [es igual a]

3 + 2 = 5

3 + 2 is **equal to** 5

larger [más grande]

2   3

A quantity of 3 is **larger** than a quantity of 2.

less [menor/menos]

9 is **less** than 11

9

11

lighter [más liviano]

lighter

H5

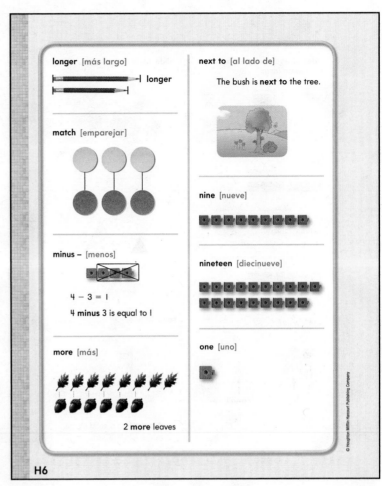

longer [más largo]

longer

match [emparejar]

minus – [menos]

4 – 3 = 1

4 **minus** 3 is equal to 1

more [más]

2 **more** leaves

next to [al lado de]

The bush is **next to** the tree.

nine [nueve]

nineteen [diecinueve]

one [uno]

H6

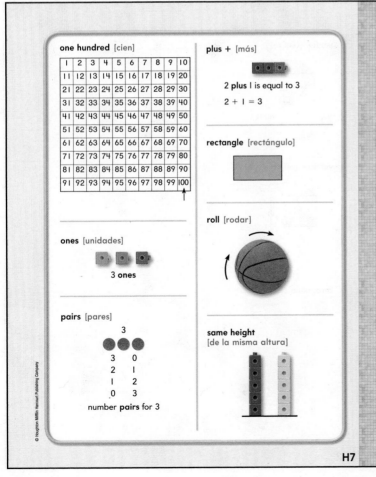

one hundred [cien]

1	2	3	4	5	6	7	8	9	10
11	12	13	14	15	16	17	18	19	20
21	22	23	24	25	26	27	28	29	30
31	32	33	34	35	36	37	38	39	40
41	42	43	44	45	46	47	48	49	50
51	52	53	54	55	56	57	58	59	60
61	62	63	64	65	66	67	68	69	70
71	72	73	74	75	76	77	78	79	80
81	82	83	84	85	86	87	88	89	90
91	92	93	94	95	96	97	98	99	100

ones [unidades]

3 **ones**

pairs [pares]

3

3	0
2	1
1	2
0	3

number **pairs** for 3

plus + [más]

2 **plus** 1 is equal to 3

2 + 1 = 3

rectangle [rectángulo]

roll [rodar]

same height [de la misma altura]

H7

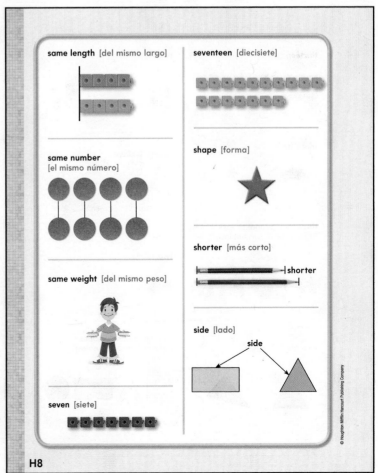

same length [del mismo largo]

same number [el mismo número]

same weight [del mismo peso]

seven [siete]

seventeen [diecisiete]

shape [forma]

shorter [más corto]

shorter

side [lado]

side

H8

Student Edition Glossary continued

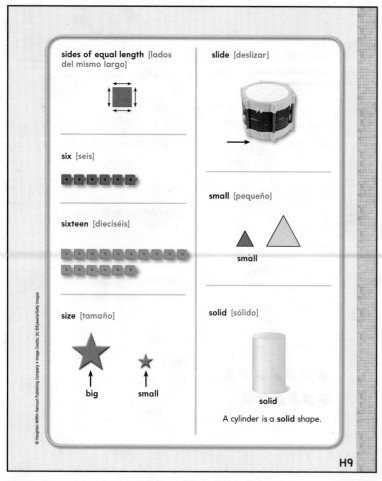

sides of equal length [lados del mismo largo]

six [seis]

sixteen [dieciséis]

size [tamaño]

big　small

slide [deslizar]

small [pequeño]

small

solid [sólido]

solid

A cylinder is a **solid** shape.

H9

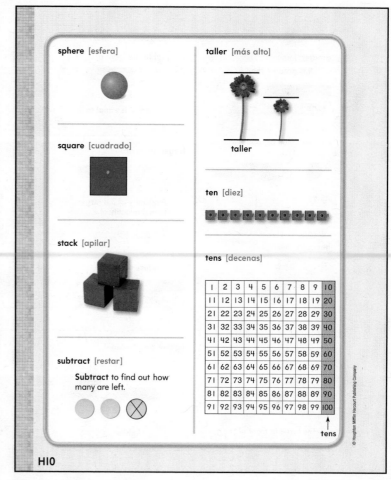

sphere [esfera]

square [cuadrado]

stack [apilar]

subtract [restar]

Subtract to find out how many are left.

taller [más alto]

taller

ten [diez]

tens [decenas]

1	2	3	4	5	6	7	8	9	10
11	12	13	14	15	16	17	18	19	20
21	22	23	24	25	26	27	28	29	30
31	32	33	34	35	36	37	38	39	40
41	42	43	44	45	46	47	48	49	50
51	52	53	54	55	56	57	58	59	60
61	62	63	64	65	66	67	68	69	70
71	72	73	74	75	76	77	78	79	80
81	82	83	84	85	86	87	88	89	90
91	92	93	94	95	96	97	98	99	100

tens

H10

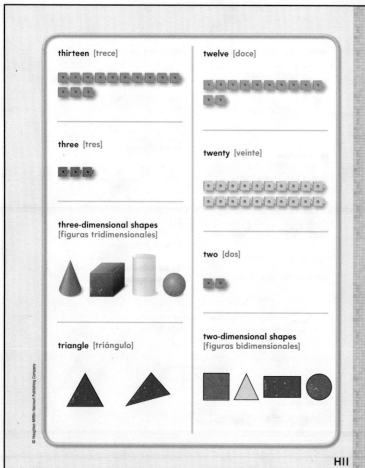

thirteen [trece]

three [tres]

three-dimensional shapes [figuras tridimensionales]

triangle [triángulo]

twelve [doce]

twenty [veinte]

two [dos]

two-dimensional shapes [figuras bidimensionales]

H11

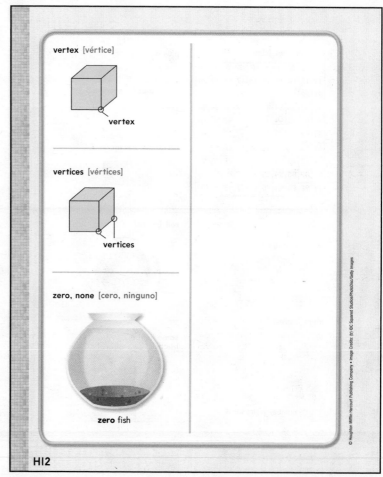

vertex [vértice]

vertex

vertices [vértices]

vertices

zero, none [cero, ninguno]

zero fish

H12

Teacher Notes

Professional Development References

Baldi, S., Jin, Y., Skemer, M., Green, P. J., & Herget, D. (2007). *Highlights from PISA 2006: Performance of U.S. 15-year-old students in science and mathematics literacy in an international context* (NCES-2008-016). National Center for Education Statistics, Institute of Education Sciences. Washington, DC: U.S. Department of Education.

Battista, M. (2007). The development of geometric and spatial thinking. In F. K. Lester (Ed.), *Second handbook of research on mathematics teaching and learning: Volume 2* (pp. 843–908). Charlotte, NC: Information Age Publishing.

Clements, D. H., & Samara, J. (2009). *Learning and teaching early math: The learning trajectories approach.* New York, NY: Routledge, Taylor, & Francis Group.

Furhman, S. H., Resnick, L., & Shepard, L. (2009). Standards aren't enough. *Education Week, 29*(7), 28.

Gonzales, P., Williams, T., Jocelyn, L., Roey, S., Katsberg, D., & Brenwald, S. (2008). *Highlights from TIMSS 2007: Mathematics and science achievement of U.S. fourth- and eighth-grade students in an international context* (NCES 2009-001 Revised). National Center for Education Statistics, Institute of Education Sciences. Washington, DC: U.S. Department of Education.

Lehrer, R. (2003). Developing understanding of measurement. In J. Kilpatrick, W. G. Martin, & D. Schifter (Eds.), *A research companion to principles and standards for school mathematics* (pp. 179–192). Reston, VA: NCTM.

Martinez, J. G. R., & Martinez, N.C. (2007). *Teaching mathematics in elementary and middle school.* Upper Saddle River, NJ: Pearson Merrill Prentice Hall.

National Council of Teachers of Mathematics. (1993). *Addenda Series: Number sense and operations, K-6.* In M. Leiva (Ed.). Reston, VA: Author.

National Council of Teachers of Mathematics (2000). *Principles and standards for school mathematics.* Reston, VA: Author.

National Council of Teachers of Mathematics. (2005). *Standards and Curriculum: A view from the nation, a joint report by the National Council of Teachers of Mathematics (NCTM) and the Association of State Supervisors of Mathematics (ASSM).* J. W. Lott & K. Nishimura (Eds.). Reston, VA: Author.

National Governors Association Center/ Council of Chief State School Officers (2010). Common Core State Standards for Mathematics. Retrieved from http://www.corestandards.org/the-standards/mathematics.

National Mathematics Advisory Panel. (2008). *Foundations for success: The final report of the National Mathematics Advisory Panel.* Washington, DC: U. S. Department of Education.

National Research Council. (2001). *Adding it up: Helping children learn mathematics.* J. Kilpatrick, J. Swafford, & B. Findell (Eds.). Washington, DC: National Academy Press.

Reed, D. S. (2009). Is there an expectations gap? Educational federalism and the demographic distribution of proficiency cut scores. *American Educational Research Journal, 46*(3), 718–742.

Reys, B. J., Chval, K., Dingman, S., McNaught, M., Regis, T. P., & Togashi, J. (2007). Grade-level learning expectations: A new challenge for elementary mathematics teachers. *Teaching Children Mathematics, 14*(1), 6–11.

Teacher Notes

Reys, R. E., Lindquist, M. M., Lambdin, D. V., Smith, N. L., & Suydam, M. N. (2004). *Helping children learn mathematics* (7th ed.). Hoboken, NJ: John Wiley & Sons.

Schneider, M. (2007). *National Assessment of Education Progress: Mapping 2005 state proficiency standards onto the NAEP scales.* Washington, DC: IES National Center for Education Statistics.

Schwartz, S. L., & Whitin, D. J. (2006). Graphing with four-year-olds: Exploring the possibilities through staff development. In G. F. Burrill & P. C. Elliott (Eds.), *Thinking and reasoning with data and chance: Sixty-eighth yearbook* (pp. 5–16). Reston, VA: NCTM.

Sheffield, L. J. & Cruikshank, D. E. (2005). *Teaching and learning mathematics: Prekindergarten through middle school.* Hoboken, NJ: John Wiley and Sons.

Triadafillidis, T. A. (1995). Circumventing visual limitations in teaching the geometry of shapes. *Educational Studies in Mathematics, 29*(3), 225–235.

Van de Walle, J. A. (2004). *Elementary and middle school mathematics: Teaching developmentally* (5th ed.). Boston, MA: Pearson Education.

Van de Walle, J. A. (2007). *Elementary and middle school mathematics: Teaching developmentally* (6th ed.). Boston, MA: Pearson Education.

Whitin, D. J. (2006). Learning to talk back to a statistic. In G. F. Burrill & P. C. Elliot (Eds.) *Thinking and reasoning with data and chance: Sixty-eighth yearbook* (pp. 31–39). Reston, VA: NCTM.

Index

About GO Math!, Program Overview, *PG4–PG11*

About the Math

If Children Ask, 137A, 155A, 187A, 243A, 397A, 409A, 441A, 499A, 523A, 535A, 573A, 655A

Teaching for Depth, 43A, 49A, 61A, 161A, 205A, 249A, 255A, 261A, 273A, 291A, 317A, 323A, 335A, 361A, 367A, 391A, 403A, 415A, 429A, 459A, 471A, 493A, 511A, 529A, 541A, 547A, 591A, 597A, 615A, 621A, 627A, 673A, 699A, 705A, 711A

Why Teach This, 13A, 19A, 31A, 37A, 67A, 81A, 87A, 93A, 119A, 125A, 131A, 167A, 181A, 199A, 217A, 231A, 267A, 297A, 311A, 347A, 447A, 465A, 505A, 579A, 609A, 615A, 649A, 667A, 687A, 693A

Above, 615–617

Activities

Advanced Learners, In every Teacher Edition lesson. Some examples are: 44, 144, 256, 362, 554, 668

ELL Vocabulary Activity. See Developing Math Language. 9H, 77F, 115H, 177H, 227H, 307H, 357H, 425H, 489H, 569H, 645F, 683F

Games. *See* Games

Grab-and-Go!™. See Grab-and-Go!™ Differentiated Centers Kit

Home. *See* Home Activity

Independent, In Grab-and-Go!™ Differentiated Centers Kit. See Differentiated Instruction

Response to Intervention. (RtI)

RtI Tier 1 and RtI Tier 2 available online.

   Tier 3 Activities. See Intensive Intervention

Vocabulary. See Vocabulary

Act Out Addition Problems, 243–246

Act Out Subtraction Problems, 323–326

Add

fluently within 5, 231A, 231–234, 243–246, 249–251, 261–264, *273A,* 273–276

Addition

add to, 231–234

equations, 255–258, 261–264, 267–270, 273–276, 279–282, 285–288, 291–294, 297–300

expressions, 231A, 237A

is equal to, *227H, 243A,* 243–244, 249, 255, 267–268, 273, 285, 297

model and draw, 249–251

number pairs, 273–276, 279–282, 285–288, 291–294, 297–300

plus, 237–240, 243–246, 249–251, 255–258, 261–264, 267–270, 273–276, 279–282, 285–288, 291–294, 297–300

problem solving, act out addition problems, 243–246

put together, 237–240

sentences, 255–258, 261–264, 267–270, 273–276, 279–282, 285–288, 291–294, 297–300

subtraction and, 347–350

ways to make ten, 193–196

word problems, 231–234, 237-240, 243–246, 258, 264, 276, 282, 288, 294, 300

Add to, 231–234

Advanced Learners, *In every Teacher Edition lesson. Some examples are: 44, 144, 256, 362, 554, 668*

Algebra

addition

   model and draw problems, 249–251

   number pairs, 273–276, 279–282, 285–288, 291–294, 297–300

   sentences, 255–258, 261–264, 267–270

   subtraction and, 347–350

classify

   and count by color, 687–690

   and count by shape, 693–696

   and count by size, 699–701

compare two-dimensional shapes, 553–556

Progress to, PG29G–PG29H

subtraction

   addition and, 347–350

   model and draw problems, 329–331

   sentences, 335–338, 341–344

ways to make 5, 49–52

ways to make 10, 193–196

Algebra Progression in GO Math! Grades K–8 and the GIMET-QR, The, Grade-Level Instructional Materials Evaluation Tool—Quality Review, *PG29A–PG29F*

Teacher Edition and Planning Guide references in *italics*; Planning Guide references begin with PG

Teacher Edition and Planning Guide references in *italics*; Planning Guide references begin with PG

Teacher Edition and Planning Guide references in *italics*; **Planning Guide references begin with PG**

Lesson at a Glance, *In every Teacher Edition lesson. Some examples are: 19A, 193A, 267A, 373A, 397A, 649A, 667A*

Lighter, 667–670

Literature, *In most Teacher Edition lessons. Some examples are: 37B, 231B, 361B, 649B. See also Grab-and-Go!™ Differentiated Centers Kit*

Longer, 649–652

Major Work of Grade K

Connecting to the Major Work, 9J, 77H, 115J, 177J, 227J, 307J, 357J, 425J, 489J, 569J, 645H, 683H

Maintaining Focus on the Major Work, 36, 72, 98, 110, 142, 172, 204, 222, 254, 302, 352, 396, 420, 452, 476, 528, 564, 602, 632, 666, 678, 704, 716

Manipulatives and Materials

Addition Fact Cards, 273B, 297B, 323B, 379B, 415B, 441B, 529B, 541B, 618B, 655B, 673B, 705B

bead string, *143B, 364, 376, 388, 400, 412, 421, 432*

Calendar, 19B, 67B, 441B, 579B

cone, *597–600*

connecting cubes, *9H, 9I, 10, 55, 77G, 78, 99, 115H, 116, 205, 206, 227H, 243B, 249, 261, 273, 279, 285, 291, 297, 305–306, 308, 310, 329, 341B, 348, 375, 403, 429, 441B, 441, 447, 453B, 471B, 541B, 597B, 612B, 612, 618B, 648, 650, 658, 699B, 705*

counters, two-color, *13, 25, 37, 49B, 49, 50–52, 61, 67, 77G, 81, 87, 93, 101, 119B, 119, 121, 131B, 131, 132, 133, 144, 145, 155, 156, 157, 178, 181, 211B, 237, 297, 307H, 308, 317, 323B, 335B, 355–356, 357H, 357I, 361, 373, 385, 397, 409, 425H, 426, 524, 536, 548, 711B, 711*

Dot Cards, 89, 93, 187B

Fifty Chart, 523B

Five Frames, 308

Graph, 707

Grid Paper, 127

Hundred Chart, 459B, 465, 471, 535B

Number and Symbol Tiles, 9H, 55B, 77G, 81B, 115H, 196, 227H, 267B, 287, 307H, 347, 357H, 425H, 489H

Number Word Cards, 19B, 31B, 37B, 119B, 125B, 131B, 155B, 161B, 181B

Numeral Cards, 10, 19A, 31B, 37B, 78, 116, 118, 119B, 125B, 131B, 155B, 161B, 177I, 177H, 178, 181B, 187B, 249B, 307H, 308, 357I, 361B, 397B, 403, 409B, 425I, 429B, 511B

Numerals, 425I, 426

Pattern Blocks, 227H, 489H, 559

Spinner, 133, 180, 501, 707

Subtraction Fact Cards, 335B, 379B, 415B, 453B, 529B, 541B, 597B, 649B, 693B

Symbol Cards, 307I

Ten Frames, 297, 425I, 426

10 × 10 Grid, 461

three-dimensional shapes, *569H, 573B, 573–576, 579B, 579, 585, 591, 597, 603–606, 609–612, 627B*

two-dimensional shapes, *489I, 493, 505, 517B, 517, 519, 529, 541, 553–556, 560, 603–606, 609–612, 615, 683F, 687, 693B, 693, 699, 707*

Workmat, 115G, 177I, 297, 357G

Matching

compare by, 99–102, 205–208

Mathematical Practices

1. Make sense of problems and persevere in solving them. In many lessons. Some examples are: 25, 37, 61, 167, 231, 243, 249, 261, 267, 311, 323, 329, 335, 341, 391, 673

2. Reason abstractly and quantitatively. In many lessons. Some examples are: 13, 19, 25, 31, 37, 43, 55, 61, 67, 87, 231, 237, 243, 249, 255, 261, 267, 273, 279, 285, 511, 523, 535, 547, 585, 591, 597, 687, 693, 699, 705

3. Construct viable arguments and critique the reasoning of others. In many lessons. Some examples are: 81, 87, 93, 99, 105, 167, 361, 373, 397, 409, 447, 609, 618, 627, 649, 655, 661, 667, 673

4. Model with mathematics. In many lessons. Some examples are: 49, 61, 99, 119, 167, 181, 193, 205, 237, 243, 249, 317, 323, 329, 391, 447, 541, 603, 615, 618, 627

5. Use appropriate tools strategically. In many lessons. Some examples are: 55, 81, 87, 93, 99, 119, 131, 143, 155, 181, 205, 237, 317, 347, 385, 429, 447, 493, 499, 505, 517, 529, 541, 553, 559, 573, 579, 585, 591, 597

6. Attend to precision. In many lessons. Some examples are: 105, 211, 217, 429, 465, 493, 499, 505, 517, 529, 573, 579, 585, 591, 597, 618, 627, 649, 655, 661, 667, 673, 687, 693, 699, 705, 711

7. Look for and make use of structure. In many lessons. Some examples are: 49, 55, 119, 131, 143, 155, 193, 255, 273, 279, 285, 291, 297, 361, 367, 373, 379, 385, 397, 511, 517, 523, 529, 535, 541, 547, 553, 559, 573, 579, 603

8. Look for and express regularity in repeated reasoning. In many lessons. Some examples are: 131, 143, 155, 205, 211, 217, 255, 347, 367, 379, 403, 415, 453, 459, 465, 471, 511, 523, 535, 547, 553, 559, 609, 705, 711

Building Mathematical Practices, 55A, 105A, 143A, 211A, 285A, 341A, 379A, 453A, 553A, 661A, 717A

Mathematical Practices, Common Core State Standards, Standards for, PG18–PG22

Mathematical Practices in GO Math! PG24–PG29

Teacher Edition and Planning Guide references in *italics*; Planning Guide references begin with PG

Teacher Edition and Planning Guide references in *italics*; Planning Guide references begin with PG

Teacher Edition and Planning Guide references in *italics*; Planning Guide references begin with PG